REVISE PEARSON EDEXC[EL]
GCSE (9–1)
Chemistry

CW00732665

GRADES 7–9
Revision & Practice

Series consultant: Harry Smith
Author: Sue Robilliard

Also available to support your revision:

Revise GCSE Study Skills Guide   9781292318875

The **Revise GCSE Study Skills Guide** is full of tried-and-trusted hints and tips for how to learn more effectively. It gives you techniques to help you achieve your best – throughout your GCSE studies and beyond.

Revise GCSE Revision Planner   9781292318868

The **Revise GCSE Revision Planner** helps you to plan and organise your time, step-by-step, throughout your GCSE revision. Use this book and wall chart to mastermind your revision.

> **For the full range of Pearson revision titles across KS2, KS3, GCSE, Functional Skills, AS/A Level and BTEC visit:**
> www.pearsonschools.co.uk/revise

Contents

Use this quick quiz to check that you are confident with the core skills and knowledge you need for the Pearson Edexcel GCSE (9–1) Chemistry Higher exam or Combined Science Higher exam.

Check your understanding with solutions to all the exam-style questions.

A small bit of small print

Pearson Edexcel publishes Sample Assessment Material and the Specification on its website. This is the official content and this book should be used in conjunction with it. The questions in the *Exam practice* sections have been written to help you revise topics and practise answering exam questions. Remember – the real exam questions may not look like this.

Welcome to Nail it!

This book provides revision and practice to help you nail down a top grade in your Pearson Edexcel GCSE (9–1) Chemistry Higher exam or Combined Science Higher exam. Designed for students aiming for a grade 7, 8 or 9, it is packed with exam tips, support for tricky topics and exam-style practice questions to make sure you are ready to tackle the toughest questions and achieve top marks.

For more help with these topics, check out these pages in the Revise Pearson Edexcel GCSE (9–1) Chemistry Higher Revision Guide. To check out pages in the Revise Pearson Edexcel GCSE (9-1) Combined Science Revision Guide see the table on page 77.

Track your progress by ticking these boxes.

Worked example exam-style questions show you exactly how to tackle tricky questions and set out your working.

Check that you are on track for a top grade with these exam-style questions. There are answers at the back of the book.

Examiner's hints give top tips for exam success.

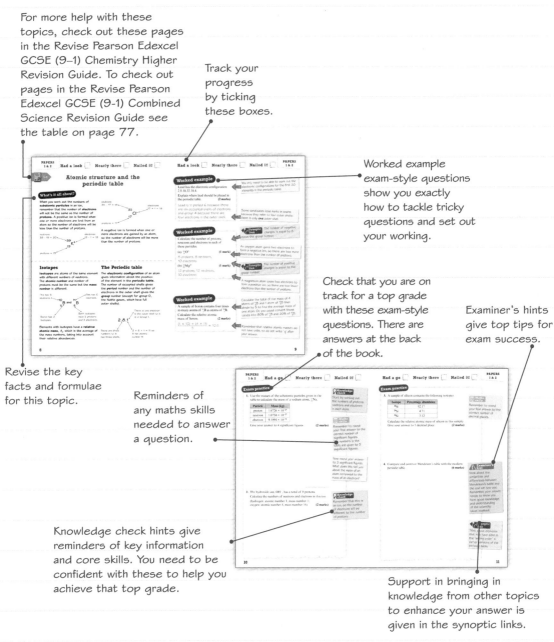

Revise the key facts and formulae for this topic.

Reminders of any maths skills needed to answer a question.

Knowledge check hints give reminders of key information and core skills. You need to be confident with these to help you achieve that top grade.

Support in bringing in knowledge from other topics to enhance your answer is given in the synoptic links.

Knowledge check

If you're aiming for a top grade, you need to be confident with core skills and knowledge, such as knowing about atomic structure, being able to balance equations and carry out mole calculations. Take this quick quiz to find out which skills you might need to brush up on before tackling the trickier topics. Answers are on page 70.

Revise core skills

Use the **Revise Pearson Edexcel GCSE (9–1) Chemistry Revision Guide** if you need to revise any of the core skills. The green arrow tell you which page in the Guide to look at for more help with each of the topics covered in the quiz.

1. Hydrogen and oxygen react to form water. What is the balanced equation for this reaction?

- **A** $2H + O \rightarrow H_2O$
- **B** $H_2 + O \rightarrow H_2O$
- **C** $H_2 + O_2 \rightarrow 2H_2O$
- **D** $2H_2 + O_2 \rightarrow 2H_2O$

2. Silver nitrate solution reacts with sodium iodide solution to form a precipitate of silver iodide and sodium nitrate solution. What is the **ionic** equation for this reaction?

- **A** $AgNO_3(aq) + NaI(aq) \rightarrow AgI(s) + NaNO_3(aq)$
- **B** $Ag^+(aq) + NaI(aq) \rightarrow AgI(s) + Na^+(aq)$
- **C** $Ag^+(aq) + I^-(aq) \rightarrow AgI(s)$
- **D** $Na^+(aq) + NO_3^-(aq) \rightarrow NaNO_3(aq)$

3. Complete this sentence.
The elements in the periodic table are arranged in order of increasing

....

4. How many electrons are there in the aluminium ion $_{13}^{27}Al^{3+}$?

- **A** 10
- **B** 16
- **C** 24
- **D** 30

5. What is the name of the compound with the formula $KClO_3$?

....

6. When do ionic compounds conduct electricity?

- **A** in aqueous solution only
- **B** in the solid state only
- **C** in aqueous solution and when molten
- **D** in the solid state and when molten

7. Carbon is in group 4 of the periodic table. How many covalent bonds can carbon atoms form?

- **A** 1
- **B** 2
- **C** 3
- **D** 4

8. Which of these is a simple molecular substance?

☐ **A** copper   ☐ **B** diamond

☐ **C** salt   ☐ **D** water

9. Which particles move through the structure when graphite conducts electricity?

☐ **A** atoms

☐ **B** electrons

☐ **C** ions

☐ **D** molecules

10. What is the relative formula mass of sulfuric acid, H_2SO_4? (A_r: H = 1, O = 16, S = 32)

....

11. The molecular formula of a compound is $C_2H_4O_2$. What is the empirical formula of this compound?

....

12. A solution is made by dissolving 5.0 g of potassium hydroxide in 100 cm^3 of water.
What is the concentration of the solution formed in g/dm^3?

☐ **A** 0.50   ☐ **B** 20

☐ **C** 50   ☐ **D** 200

13. What is the amount, in mol, of methane molecules in 96 g of methane, CH_4? (A_r: H = 1, C = 12)

☐ **A** 0.167   ☐ **B** 2

☐ **C** 4   ☐ **D** 6

14. How many **atoms** are there in 0.5 mol of nitrogen gas, N_2? (Avogadro's constant = 6.02×10^{23})

☐ **A** 3.01×10^{23}

☐ **B** 6.02×10^{23}

☐ **C** 1.204×10^{24}

☐ **D** 2.408×10^{24}

15. Which ions are present in aqueous solutions of all acids?

☐ **A** Cl^- ☐ **B** H^+

☐ **C** Na^+ ☐ **D** SO_4^{2-}

16. The concentration of an aqueous solution of an acid is decreased by a factor of 100. What is the change in pH of the solution?

☐ **A** decrease by 1

☐ **B** decrease by 2

☐ **C** increase by 1

☐ **D** increase by 2

17. Which of these reacts with dilute sulfuric acid to form magnesium sulfate and hydrogen?

☐ **A** magnesium

☐ **B** magnesium carbonate

☐ **C** magnesium hydroxide

☐ **D** magnesium oxide

18. Which of these is an insoluble salt?

☐ **A** ammonium nitrate

☐ **B** barium sulfate

☐ **C** potassium chloride

☐ **D** sodium carbonate

19. What is produced at the **cathode** during the electrolysis of molten zinc chloride?

- [ ] **A** chlorine
- [ ] **B** hydrogen
- [ ] **C** oxygen
- [ ] **D** zinc

20. What is produced at the **anode** during the electrolysis of an aqueous solution of sodium sulfate?

- [ ] **A** hydrogen
- [ ] **B** oxygen
- [ ] **C** sodium
- [ ] **D** sulfur

21. Four metals are arranged in order of decreasing reactivity from left to right: potassium, calcium, zinc, silver. Which atoms form cations most easily?

- [ ] **A** potassium atoms
- [ ] **B** calcium atoms
- [ ] **C** zinc atoms
- [ ] **D** silver atoms

22. Zinc is formed when zinc oxide is heated with carbon.

$ZnO + C \rightarrow Zn + CO$

Which substance is reduced in this reaction?

- [ ] **A** ZnO
- [ ] **B** C
- [ ] **C** Zn
- [ ] **D** CO

23. Which of these is a typical property of a transition metal?

- [ ] **A** can act as a catalyst
- [ ] **B** forms white or colourless compounds
- [ ] **C** has a low density
- [ ] **D** has a low melting point

24. During an accurate titration, $25.0\,cm^3$ of sodium hydroxide solution reacted with $22.6\,cm^3$ of hydrochloric acid. Which of these should be used to measure the volume of sodium hydroxide solution?

- [ ] **A** burette
- [ ] **B** conical flask
- [ ] **C** measuring cylinder
- [ ] **D** pipette

25. A student obtained the following titres during a titration: $22.3\,cm^3$, $21.9\,cm^3$, $21.5\,cm^3$, $21.6\,cm^3$. What is the mean of the concordant titres?

- [ ] **A** $21.55\,cm^3$
- [ ] **B** $21.67\,cm^3$
- [ ] **C** $21.83\,cm^3$
- [ ] **D** $22.10\,cm^3$

26. What mass of sodium hydroxide, NaOH, is needed to make $100\,cm^3$ of a solution with a concentration of $0.100\,mol/dm^3$? (M_r of NaOH $= 40$)

- [ ] **A** $0.4\,g$
- [ ] **B** $4.0\,g$
- [ ] **C** $40\,g$
- [ ] **D** $400\,g$

27. What is the amount, in mol, of hydrochloric acid in $25.0\,cm^3$ of a solution of hydrochloric acid with a concentration of $0.200\,mol/dm^3$?

....

28. The theoretical yield of iron produced in a reaction is $5.6\,g$. The actual yield of iron formed is $3.5\,g$. What is the percentage yield of iron in this reaction?

....

29 Methanol, CH_3OH, is manufactured by this reaction

$$CO(g) + 2H_2(g) \rightleftharpoons CH_3OH(g)$$

The forward reaction is exothermic. What are the effects of increasing the temperature on this equilibrium?

☐ **A** rate of reaction decreases and less methanol is formed

☐ **B** rate of reaction decreases and more methanol is formed

☐ **C** rate of reaction increases and less methanol is formed

☐ **D** rate of reaction increases and more methanol is formed

30. Chlorine displaces bromine from aqueous potassium bromide. The half equations for this reaction are

$$Cl_2(aq) + 2e^- \rightarrow 2Cl^-(aq)$$
$$2Br^-(aq) \rightarrow Br_2(aq) + 2e^-$$

Which species is oxidised?

☐ **A** Cl_2 ☐ **B** Cl^-

☐ **C** Br^- ☐ **D** Br_2

31. Complete the sentence.

The ....the rate of reaction,

the lower the .... time.

32. Which of these is always endothermic?

☐ **A** displacement

☐ **B** dissolving

☐ **C** neutralisation

☐ **D** thermal decomposition

33. Which of these formulae represents a hydrocarbon?

☐ **A** C_3H_8 ☐ **B** CH_2Cl_2

☐ **C** C_2H_6O ☐ **D** $NaHCO_3$

34. Which of these functional groups is needed to form an addition polymer?

☐ **A** alcohols and carboxylic acids

☐ **B** alcohols only

☐ **C** alkanes and alkenes

☐ **D** alkenes only

35. Which of these carboxylic acids will react with magnesium to form magnesium propanoate?

☐ **A** HCOOH

☐ **B** CH_3COOH

☐ **C** CH_3CH_2COOH

☐ **D** $CH_3CH_2CH_2COOH$

36. A compound reacts with aqueous sodium hydroxide when heated and releases a gas that turns damp red litmus blue. Which of these ions could be present in the compound?

☐ **A** N^{3-} ☐ **B** Na^+

☐ **C** NH_4^+ ☐ **D** NO_3^-

1–3, 11

Formulae and equations

What's it all about?

Balancing formulae

In the formula of an ionic compound, the charges must be balanced. An ammonium ion is NH_4^+ and a sulfate ion is SO_4^{2-}. The formula for ammonium sulfate is:

Brackets are needed when there is more than one compound ion in a formula.

$(NH_4)_2SO_4$

2 ammonium ions with 1 positive charge each balance the 2 negative charges on the sulfate ion.

A compound ion contains more than one atom, for example:
NH_4^+, OH^-, NO_3^-, CO_3^{2-}, SO_4^{2-}

Balancing equations

All equations must be balanced so they have the same number of atoms of each kind on each side.

$H_2 + O_2 \rightarrow H_2O$

This equation is not balanced as there are 2 hydrogen atoms and 2 oxygen atoms on the left and 2 hydrogen atoms and 1 oxygen atom on the right.

$2H_2 + O_2 \rightarrow 2H_2O$

Add a 2 in front of H_2O to give 2 oxygen atoms on the right. A 2 is now needed in front of H_2 to balance the hydrogen.

All ionic equations must be balanced in terms of the numbers of atoms or ions of each element **and** their charges.

$Cu + Ag^+ \rightarrow Ag + Cu^{2+}$

This ionic equation is balanced in terms of particles as there is 1 copper particle on each side and 1 silver particle on each side of the equation.

It is not balanced in terms of charges as there is only 1 positive charge on the left but 2 on the right.

The correct balanced equation is
$$Cu + 2Ag^+ \rightarrow 2Ag + Cu^{2+}$$

There are now two positive charges on each side of the equation.

Worked example

Balance this equation.

$C_4H_{10} + O_2 \rightarrow CO_2 + H_2O$ **(1 mark)**

$C_4H_{10} + 6\frac{1}{2}O_2 \rightarrow 4CO_2 + 5H_2O$

Start by balancing the carbon atoms, then the hydrogen atoms and finally the oxygen atoms. It is acceptable to balance equations like this using $\frac{1}{2}$.

Worked example

Balance this ionic equation.

$Br_2 + I^- \rightarrow Br^- + I_2$ **(1 mark)**

$Br_2 + 2I^- \rightarrow 2Br^- + I_2$

This equation is balanced in terms of charges but not in terms of atoms.

Exam practice

Use the formulae of the ions you are given.

1. The symbols of some ions are:

| Na^+ Mg^{2+} Al^{3+} NO_3^- OH^- SO_4^{2-} |

Write the formulae for the following compounds:

(a) sodium sulfate .... **(1 mark)**

Knowledge check

Remember to use brackets if you need more than one of any compound ion.

(b) magnesium hydroxide .... **(1 mark)**

Examiner's hint

The total numbers of positive charges and negative charges must be the same.

(c) aluminium nitrate .... **(1 mark)**

2. Balance these equations by inserting numbers where appropriate.

(a) .....Na + ... $H_2O \rightarrow$ .....NaOH + ...H_2 **(1 mark)**

You do not need to insert the number 1 when balancing equations.

(b) .....Fe + ...$Cl_2 \rightarrow FeCl_3$ **(1 mark)**

(c) .....C_2H_6 + ...$O_2 \rightarrow$ .....CO_2 + ...H_2O **(1 mark)**

It is acceptable to balance equations like this using $\frac{1}{2}$.

3. Magnesium reacts with dilute nitric acid to form a solution of magnesium nitrate and hydrogen.

Write the balanced equation for this reaction. Include state symbols. **(3 marks)**

The formulae of the ions in question 1 will help you to work out the formula of magnesium nitrate.

4. Complete and balance these ionic equations.

(a) .....Cl_2 + ...$Br^- \rightarrow$ .....Cl^- + ...Br_2 **(1 mark)**

Remember to check that the particles and the charges are balanced.

(b) .....Al^{3+} + ... $\rightarrow$ .....$Al(OH)_3$ **(2 marks)**

(c) .....Pb^{2+} + ... $\rightarrow$ .....PbI_2 **(2 marks)**

Atomic structure and the periodic table

What's it all about?

When you work out the numbers of **subatomic particles** in an ion, remember that the number of **electrons** will not be the same as the number of **protons**. A positive ion is formed when one or more electrons are lost from an atom so the number of electrons will be less than the number of protons.

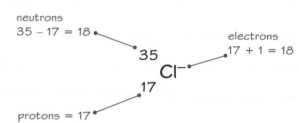

neutrons
35 – 17 = 18

35

Cl⁻

17

electrons
17 + 1 = 18

protons = 17

A negative ion is formed when one or more electrons are gained by an atom, so the number of electrons will be more than the number of protons.

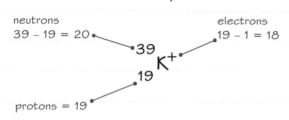

neutrons
39 – 19 = 20

39

K⁺

19

electrons
19 – 1 = 18

protons = 19

Isotopes

Isotopes are atoms of the same element with different numbers of neutrons. The **atomic number** and number of protons must be the same but the **mass number** is different.

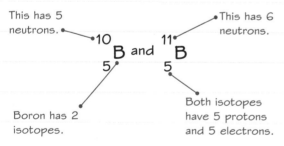

This has 5 neutrons.

$^{10}_{5}$B and $^{11}_{5}$B

This has 6 neutrons.

Boron has 2 isotopes.

Both isotopes have 5 protons and 5 electrons.

Elements with isotopes have a **relative atomic mass**, A_r, which is the average of the mass numbers, taking into account their relative abundances.

The Periodic table

The **electronic configuration** of an atom gives information about the position of the element in the **periodic table**. The number of occupied shells gives the **period** number and the number of electrons in the outer shell gives the **group** number (except for group 0, the Noble gases, which have full outer shells).

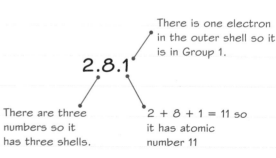

There is one electron in the outer shell so it is in Group 1.

2.8.1

There are three numbers so it has three shells.

2 + 8 + 1 = 11 so it has atomic number 11

Worked example

Lead has the electronic configuration 2.8.18.32.18.4.

Explain where lead should be placed in the periodic table. **(2 marks)**

Lead is in period 6 because there are six occupied shells of electrons and group 4 because there are four electrons in the outer shell.

 You only need to be able to work out the electronic configurations for the first 20 elements in the periodic table.

 Some candidates lose marks in exams because they refer to four outer shells: there is only **one** outer shell.

Worked example

Calculate the number of protons, neutrons and electrons in each of these particles.

(a) $^{16}_{8}O^{2-}$ **(1 mark)**

8 protons, 8 neutrons, 10 electrons

(b) $^{24}_{12}Mg^{2+}$ **(1 mark)**

12 protons, 12 neutrons, 10 electrons

Synoptic link The number of negative charges is equal to 8 minus the group number.

 An oxygen atom gains two electrons to form a negative ion, so there are two more electrons than the number of protons.

Synoptic link The number of positive charges is equal to the group number.

A magnesium atom loses two electrons to form a positive ion, so there are two fewer electrons than the number of protons.

Worked example

A sample of boron contains four times as many atoms of $^{11}_{5}B$ as atoms of $^{10}_{5}B$. Calculate the relative atomic mass of boron. **(2 marks)**

$$\frac{(1 \times 10) + (4 \times 11)}{5} = 10.8$$

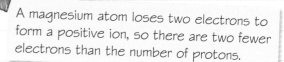 Calculate the total of the mass of 4 atoms of $^{11}_{5}B$ and 1 atom of $^{10}_{5}B$ then divide by 5 to find the average mass of one atom. Or, you could convert these values into 80% of $^{11}_{5}B$ and 20% of $^{10}_{5}B$.

 Remember that relative atomic masses do not have units, so do not write 'g' after your answer.

Exam practice

1. Use the masses of the subatomic particles given in the table to calculate the mass of a sodium atom, $^{23}_{11}Na$.

Particle	Mass (kg)
proton	1.6726×10^{-27}
neutron	1.6750×10^{-27}
electron	9.1094×10^{-31}

Give your answer to 4 significant figures.   **(2 marks)**

Knowledge check

Start by working out the numbers of protons, neutrons and electrons in each atom.

Maths skills

Remember to round your final answer to the correct number of significant figures. The numbers in the table are given to 5 significant figures.

Now round your answer to 3 significant figures. What does this tell you about the mass of an atom compared to the mass of an electron?

....

2. The hydroxide ion, OH^-, has a total of 9 protons. Calculate the numbers of neutrons and electrons in this ion.

(hydrogen: atomic number 1, mass number 1; oxygen: atomic number 8, mass number 16)   **(2 marks)**

Knowledge check

Remember that this is an ion, so the number of electrons will be different to the number of protons.

Exam practice

3. A sample of silicon contains the following isotopes.

Isotope	Percentage abundance
^{28}Si	92.17
^{29}Si	4.71
^{30}Si	3.12

Calculate the relative atomic mass of silicon in this sample.
Give your answer to 1 decimal place.   **(2 marks)**

Maths skills

Remember to round your final answer to the correct number of decimal places.

4. Compare and contrast Mendeleev's table with the modern periodic table.   **(6 marks)**

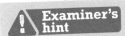

Examiner's hint

Think about the similarities and differences between Mendeleev's table and the one we now use. Remember, your answer needs to show you have good knowledge and understanding of the scientific ideas involved.

Synoptic link

Think about elements that may have been in the 'wrong order' in earlier versions of the periodic table.

Bonding

What's it all about?

Bonding is the strong electrostatic forces of attraction between oppositely charged particles. The **outer** electrons of atoms are rearranged and usually obtain the same electron configuration as the nearest noble gas. They do this by gaining, losing or sharing electrons.

Types of bonding

Ionic bonding:

Covalent bonding:

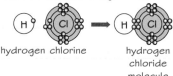

hydrogen chlorine   hydrogen chloride molecule

Metallic bonding:

positive ions

delocalised electrons

✓ takes place between metals and non-metals

✓ involves the transfer of electrons from the metal to the non-metal - metals form cations (positive ions) and non-metals usually form anions (negative ions)

✓ is the strong electrostatic attraction between oppositely charged ions

✓ takes place between non-metals

✓ involves the sharing of pairs of electrons to form a molecule

✓ is the strong electrostatic attraction between two nuclei and the shared pair of electrons

The resulting particle is a molecule.

✓ takes place in metals

✓ involves positive ions in a sea of electrons

✓ is the strong electrostatic attraction between metal ions and delocalised electrons

The electrons are free to move between the positive ions.

Metals form cations (positive ions) and non-metals usually form anions (negative ions). Hydrogen is a non-metal but forms an H^+ ion.

Ionic and covalent bonding

Similarities	Differences
• Both types of bonding involve the rearrangement of the outer electrons of atoms.	• Ionic bonding takes place when electrons are gained and lost. Anions and cations are formed.
• They are both strong. • Atoms or ions usually have 8 electrons in their outer shell once they have bonded.	• Covalent bonding takes place when pairs of electrons are shared. Neutral molecules are formed.

Worked example

Aluminium chloride consists of covalent molecules that can be represented by this structure:

(a) Write the electronic configurations of aluminium and chlorine. **(2 marks)**

Aluminium is 2.8.3 and chlorine is 2.8.7.

> Look at a copy of the periodic table to find the atomic numbers.

> Aluminium has 13 electrons and chlorine has 17 electrons.

(b) Draw a dot-and-cross diagram to represent aluminium chloride. Show the outer shell electrons only. **(1 mark)**

> You could also draw the electrons in overlapping circles. Don't forget to include the 3 non-bonding pairs of electrons on each chlorine atom.

(c) State **two** features that are unusual about this molecule. **(2 marks)**

Metals and non-metals react together to form ionic compounds but this is a covalent molecule.

There are only 6 electrons in the outer shell of aluminium in aluminium chloride but a complete outer shell holds 8 electrons.

> Don't be tempted to add 2 more electrons to the outer shell of aluminium.

Exam practice

1. Sodium oxide is an ionic compound.

   Describe, in terms of electron transfer, how sodium atoms react with oxygen atoms to form sodium oxide.

   You may include diagrams in your answer.   **(4 marks)**

Examiner's hint

Use the information given in the question. Sodium oxide is an ionic compound so you should not mention sharing electrons.

Knowledge check

Metals form positive ions and non-metals form negative ions.

Synoptic link

Start with the electronic configurations of sodium and oxygen – use the periodic table to work out how many electrons they each have.

Diagrams are not essential but may help you to organise your answer. You could include dot-and-cross diagrams to show the electronic configurations of the atoms and the ions. Don't forget to include the charges on the ions.

Exam practice

2. Magnesium is a metal and chlorine is a non-metal.

Compare and contrast the bonding in magnesium with that in chlorine gas.

You may include diagrams in your answer. **(6 marks)**

Examiner's hint

'Compare and contrast' means that you need to include similarities and differences. You need to include at least one similarity and at least one difference in your answer.

Knowledge check

Think about the types of bonding in magnesium and chlorine gas. If you cannot remember the particles in chlorine gas, revise group 7.

Synoptic link

Don't just describe the bonding in magnesium and then the bonding in chlorine. It isn't wrong to include these, but you also need to think about the similarities and the differences between them and make these clear in your answer.

It is often helpful to include diagrams when describing the bonding in a substance.

12,
14–18, 25,
111, 112

Structure, bonding and properties

What's it all about?

Giant lattice structures

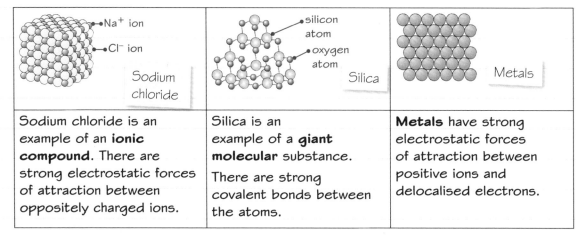

• Na⁺ ion	• silicon atom	
• Cl⁻ ion	• oxygen atom	
Sodium chloride	Silica	Metals

Sodium chloride is an example of an **ionic compound**. There are strong electrostatic forces of attraction between oppositely charged ions.	Silica is an example of a **giant molecular** substance. There are strong covalent bonds between the atoms.	**Metals** have strong electrostatic forces of attraction between positive ions and delocalised electrons.

Simple molecular

Poly(ethene) is an example of a simple molecular substance.

There are strong covalent bonds in the molecules.

There are weak forces **between** the molecules (intermolecular forces).

Physical properties

The physical properties of a substance depend on bonding and structure. The uses of a material depend on its properties.

Physical property	Explanation
High melting point or boiling point	A lot of energy is needed to overcome the forces between the particles to separate them. Ionic compounds, giant molecular substances and most metals have high melting and boiling points.
Conducts electricity	Ionic compounds conduct electricity when molten or dissolved in water as their ions can move. Metals and graphite conduct electricity, as delocalised electrons can move.
Soluble in water	Many ionic compounds and a few simple molecular substances are soluble in water because particles form strong forces with water molecules. Metals and giant molecular substances are not soluble in water.

Worked example

Potassium chloride and carbon dioxide have very different properties.

Potassium chloride is an ionic compound. It is a crystalline solid with a high melting point and conducts electricity when molten or in aqueous solution.

Carbon dioxide is a covalent compound. It is a gas at room temperature and does not conduct electricity.

Explain these properties of potassium chloride and carbon dioxide in terms of the particles present and the forces between them. **(6 marks)**

Potassium chloride contains ions / K^+ and Cl^-. It has a high melting point because it has a giant structure with strong (electrostatic) forces of attraction between the ions so a lot of energy is needed to separate the oppositely charged ions.
It conducts electricity when molten or in aqueous solution because the ions are free to move.

Carbon dioxide contains molecules so little energy is needed to separate the molecules. It has a low melting point because it is a simple molecular substance with weak forces between the molecules. It does not conduct electricity as it does not contain any charged particles (that are free to move from place to place).

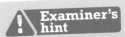

Examiner's hint

You do not need to include any other properties, just write about melting points and conduction of electricity.

You do not need to explain how these particles are formed from the atoms.

Remember that **ions** move in an ionic compound, not electrons.

Remember that covalent bonds are **not** broken when a simple molecular substance melts or boils.

Exam practice

1. Explain why solid magnesium sulfate does not conduct electricity but an aqueous solution of magnesium sulfate is a good conductor of electricity.   **(2 marks)**

Examiner's hint
Take care to include the correct particles in your answer.

2. Graphite and ceramics have very high melting points. However, graphite is a good conductor of electricity but ceramics are poor conductors when solid.

   Discuss these two properties, in terms of structure and bonding.   **(4 marks)**

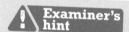
Examiner's hint
You need to explain the similarities and differences in their structure and bonding and relate these to the properties.

Knowledge check
Revise the structure and bonding in graphite.

Synoptic link
You are not expected to know a lot about ceramics but apply your knowledge of the properties to predict the likely structure.

Exam practice

3. Some physical properties of three substances, **A**, **B** and **C** are given in the table.

Property	A	B	C
Melting point in °C	650	801	42
Conducts electricity	good conductor when solid	poor conductor when solid good conductor when molten	poor conductor when solid and molten

Identify the types of bonding and structure in **A**, **B** and **C**.

Justify your answers. **(6 marks)**

The melting point of graphite is over 3500°C.

Knowledge check

The bonding is ionic, covalent or metallic. The structure is giant or simple molecular.

Synoptic link

Use the relative melting points to consider the strength of the bonds or forces between particles. Then use the conduction to consider the particles.

You must give reasons for your answers and you must also present these reasons clearly and in a logical structure.

34–41

Acids, bases and salts

What's it all about?

Bases

Bases react with an acid to form a salt and water. Metal oxides and metal hydroxides are bases.

An **alkali** is a base that is soluble in water, e.g. sodium hydroxide (NaOH) and potassium hydroxide (KOH).

The pH depends on the concentration of the solution and the strength of the acid or alkali.

Acids and alkalis

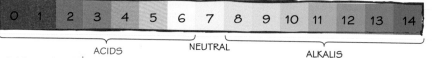

|0 1 2 3 4 5 6 | 7 | 8 9 10 11 12 13 14|
|ACIDS|NEUTRAL|ALKALIS|

Acids produce H^+ ions in an aqueous solution. The pH of aqueous solution is <7. The higher the concentration of H^+(aq) ions, the **lower** the pH.

Alkalis produce OH^- ions in an aqueous solution. The pH of aqueous solution is >7. The higher the concentration of OH^-(aq) ions, the **higher** the pH.

Leave out the symbols of the ions in solution that do not change.

Strong acids

A **strong acid** completely dissociates into ions in aqueous solution. Hydrochloric acid (HCl), nitric acid (HNO_3) and sulfuric acid (H_2SO_4) are strong acids. A **weak acid** only slightly dissociates into ions in aqueous solution. Ethanoic acid (CH_3COOH) is a weak acid.

Ionic equations for reactions of acids

$$2H^+(aq) + Mg(s) \rightarrow Mg^{2+}(aq) + H_2(g)$$
$$2H^+(aq) + CuO(s) \rightarrow Cu^{2+}(aq) + H_2O(l)$$
$$H^+(aq) + OH^-(aq) \rightarrow H_2O(l)$$
$$2H^+(aq) + CuCO_3(s) \rightarrow Cu^{2+}(aq) + CO_2(g) + H_2O(l)$$

Salts

A **salt** is formed when the hydrogen ions in an acid are replaced with metal ions. For example, nitric acid forms nitrates and ethanoic acid forms ethanoates. Soluble salts can be made by reacting an acid with a base, an alkali or a carbonate. Some moderately reactive metals, such as magnesium, also react with acids to form salts.

Insoluble salts

Insoluble salts are made by mixing together an aqueous solution containing the cation and an aqueous solution containing the anion in the required salt. For example, silver chloride can be made from silver nitrate solution and sodium chloride solution.

$$Ag^+(aq) + Cl^-(aq) \rightarrow AgCl(s)$$

Worked example

The pH values of four solutions are given.
Which solution contains the highest
concentration of hydrogen ions?

☒ **A** pH = 1.0

☐ **B** pH = 2.0

☐ **C** pH = 11.0

☐ **D** pH = 13.0　　　　　　**(1 mark)**

Worked example

Excess magnesium oxide was added to dilute
sulfuric acid in a beaker. The mixture was
warmed and stirred.

magnesium + sulfuric → magnesium + water
oxide　　　　acid　　　　　sulfate

(a) Write the ionic equation for this reaction.
Include state symbols.　　**(2 marks)**

$2H^+(aq) + MgO(s) \rightarrow Mg^{2+}(aq) + H_2O(l)$

(b) Describe how a sample of pure, dry
magnesium sulfate crystals can be
obtained from the mixture of magnesium
sulfate solution and excess magnesium
oxide in the beaker.　　**(4 marks)**

Filter the mixture to remove the excess
magnesium oxide. Collect the filtrate
of magnesium sulfate solution in an
evaporating basin. Heat the basin until
about half of the water has evaporated.
Leave the basin to cool down and for the
crystals to form. Dry the crystals between
filter papers or in a warm oven.

Exam practice

1. A student wrote the following method for carrying out a titration to determine the exact volume of hydrochloric acid needed to neutralise 25.00 cm³ of sodium hydroxide solution.

- Measure 25.00 cm³ of hydrochloric acid in a measuring cylinder and pour it into a conical flask.
- Add a few drops of methyl orange to the hydrochloric acid.
- Rinse a burette with sodium hydroxide solution then fill it to the 0 mark.
- Add the sodium hydroxide to the hydrochloric acid while swirling the conical flask.
- Stop adding the sodium hydroxide when the methyl orange turns green.
- Note the volume of sodium hydroxide solution added.
- Repeat the titration until two concordant volumes are obtained.

(a) Identify **three** errors in this method and state what the student should have written. **(3 marks)**

(b) Explain **two** further practical details to improve the accuracy of the titration. **(4 marks)**

Examiner's hint

Read the introductory sentence carefully and check to make sure the student's method can be used to solve this problem.

Examiner's hint

Don't just state what is wrong, include what the student should have done to correct the errors.

The command word 'explain' means that you have to give reasons for your answers.

Knowledge check

Think about the apparatus needed to carry out an accurate titration.

Exam practice

2. This question is about insoluble salts.

   (a) Give the names of two soluble salts that could be used to prepare a sample of barium sulfate. **(2 marks)**

   (b) Aqueous solutions of sodium chloride and lead nitrate are mixed together.

      (i) Predict the name of the precipitate formed.
      (1 mark)

      (ii) Write the ionic equation for this reaction. Include state symbols. **(3 marks)**

      (iii) Describe how you would obtain a pure, dry sample of the insoluble salt formed after the sodium chloride and lead nitrate solutions are mixed. **(3 marks)**

⚠ **Examiner's hint**

Remember that all sodium, potassium and ammonium salts and all nitrates are soluble. So, to make an insoluble salt XY, choose X nitrate and sodium (or potassium or ammonium) Y as your two soluble reactants.

You need to learn the solubility rules.

💡 **Knowledge check**

Just include the ions that form the precipitate and don't forget to include the state symbols.

⚠ **Examiner's hint**

This is a common, straightforward question, but you need to include all the practical details to get a good mark. Many students do not make sure that the sample is pure.

19–22,
24, 62,
63

Calculations with masses

What's it all about?

The **molecular formula** of a compound shows the actual number of atoms of each element in a molecule of a compound. It is an exact multiple of the **empirical formula**.

To calculate the amount, in mol, of a substance from its mass, use the equation: amount (mol) $= \dfrac{\text{mass (g)}}{M_r}$

Substances react together in the mole ratio shown in a **stoichiometric** (balanced) equation. Usually, one of the reactants is present in excess so some of it will be left over at the end.

$MgCO_3(s) + 2HCl(aq) \rightarrow$
$MgCl_2(aq) + H_2O(l) + CO_2(g)$

The stoichiometric equation shows that the mole ratio of $MgCO_3 : HCl = 1:2$; that is, this is the ratio of the balancing numbers. If there is excess magnesium carbonate, some of it will remain as a solid at the end of the reaction. If there is excess hydrochloric acid, all of the magnesium carbonate will react.

Worked example

The empirical formula of a compound is CH_2 and the relative formula mass is 98. Determine the molecular formula of this compound.

(relative atomic masses: H = 1, C = 12)   **(1 mark)**

M_r of $CH_2 = 12 + (2 \times 1) = 14$

$\dfrac{98}{14} = 7$

molecular formula is C_7H_{14}

It would be incorrect to write $7CH_2$ as this shows seven separate CH_2 particles. The molecular formula shows the actual number of atoms of each element in one molecule of the compound.

Worked example

Calculate the amount, in mol, of 22 tonnes of carbon dioxide, CO_2.

(relative atomic masses: C = 12, O = 16) **(1 mark)**

mass of $CO_2 = 22 \times 10^6 g$

M_r of $CO_2 = 12 + (2 \times 16) = 44$

amount of $CO_2 = \dfrac{22 \times 10^6}{44}$

$= 500\,000$ or 5×10^5 mol

Remember to convert the mass into grams if you are given it in kilograms or tonnes. There are $1 \times 10^6 g$ in 1 tonne.

Exam practice

1. Calculate the amount, in mol, of 180 kg of iron(II) hydroxide, $Fe(OH)_2$ in 180 kg of it.

   (relative atomic masses: H = 1, O = 16, Fe = 56)

   (2 marks)

Examiner's hint

Remember to multiply the relative atomic masses of the particles inside the bracket by the number outside the bracket in the formula.

Knowledge check

1 kg = 1000 g or 1×10^3 g

2. In an experiment, 1.2 g of magnesium reacted with a solution containing 6.0 g sulfuric acid to form 5.2 g of magnesium sulfate.

   $$Mg + H_2SO_4 \rightarrow MgSO_4 + H_2$$

   (a) Show, by calculation, that the sulfuric acid is in excess.

   (4 marks)

Examiner's hint

Start by calculating the amounts, in mol, of magnesium and sulfuric acid.

   (b) Calculate the percentage yield of magnesium sulfate.

   (relative atomic masses: H = 1, O = 16, Mg = 24, S = 32)

   (3 marks)

Examiner's hint

Start by calculating the theoretical yield.

Knowledge check

Remember, you will need to know how to calculate a percentage yield.

64–65

Calculations with gas volumes

What's it all about?

Avogadro's law

This law states that equal volumes of all gases, at the same temperature and pressure, contain the same number of molecules. This can be reversed so that equal numbers of molecules or moles of any gas, at the same temperature and pressure, occupy the same volume.
It doesn't matter how many atoms there are in the molecules, it is the number of molecules or moles that determines the volume. For example, 1 mol of He, H_2, NH_3 and CH_4 all occupy the same volume at the same temperature and pressure.

Molar gas volume

The **molar gas volume** is the volume occupied by one mole of any gas. It is $24\,000\,cm^3$ or $24\,dm^3$ at room temperature and atmospheric pressure (rtp).

The amount, in moles, of gas is calculated using the equation

$$\text{amount of gas (mol)} = \frac{\text{volume of gas}}{\text{molar volume}}$$

The volumes can be in cm^3 or dm^3 but both must be in the same unit.

Worked example

Calculate the volume of hydrogen needed to react completely with $50\,cm^3$ of oxygen.

$2H_2(g) + O_2(g) \rightarrow 2H_2O(g)$

(all volumes of gases are measured under the same conditions of temperature and pressure)   **(1 mark)**

2 mol of hydrogen reacts with 1 mol of oxygen, so $2 \times 50 = 100\,cm^3$ of hydrogen reacts with $50\,cm^3$ of oxygen.

When an equation just involves gases, you do not need to convert the volume to moles, just use Avogadro's law. The ratio of gas volumes is the same as the ratio of moles (balancing numbers).

Worked example

Calculate the volume of 0.125 mol of nitrogen at rtp.   **(1 mark)**

volume of gas = amount of gas × molar volume

$$= 0.125 \times 24 = 3\,dm^3$$

or $0.125 \times 24\,000 = 3000\,cm^3$

Make sure that both volumes are in the same units.

Exam practice

1. Ethane reacts with oxygen as shown in the equation

$$C_2H_6(g) + 3\tfrac{1}{2}O_2(g) \rightarrow 2CO_2(g) + 3H_2O(l)$$

Calculate the total volume of gases left at the end of the reaction between $100\,cm^3$ of ethane and $500\,cm^3$ of oxygen.

(all volumes of gases are measured under the same conditions of temperature and pressure)   **(3 marks)**

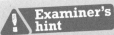
Examiner's hint

Check to see if one of the gases is in excess by calculating the volume of oxygen that will react with $100\,cm^3$ of ethane.

Knowledge check

Remember that it is acceptable to balance equations like this using $\tfrac{1}{2}$.

Knowledge check

Water is a liquid so you can ignore its volume in this question.

2. $22\,g$ of a gas has a volume of $12\,dm^3$ at rtp.

Calculate the relative formula mass of this gas.   **(1 mark)**

Synoptic link

You will need to know how to do calculations with masses to answer this question.

3. Calculate the number of **atoms** in $120\,cm^3$ of sulfur dioxide, SO_2.   **(3 marks)**

Remember to calculate the number of atoms, not just the number of molecules.

Knowledge check

You will need to use Avogadro's constant 6.02×10^{23}.

Calculations with concentrations of solutions

What's it all about?

The concentration of a solution can be expressed in $g\ dm^{-3}$ or $mol\ dm^{-3}$.
They are related by the equation:

$$\text{concentration in mol dm}^{-3} = \frac{\text{concentration in mol/dm}^3}{M_r \text{ of solute}}$$

If the volume is given in cm^3, remember to divide it by 1000 to convert it to dm^3.

To calculate the amount, in mol, of a solute in a specific volume of solution, use the equation:

amount of solute (mol) = concentration (mol/dm³) × volume (dm³)

Worked example

Calculate the concentration in mol/dm³ of a solution of sulfuric acid, H_2SO_4, that contains 2.45 g in 500 cm³ of solute.

(relative atomic masses: H = 1, O = 16, S = 32) **(2 marks)**

Start by calculating the concentration of solution in g/dm³. Remember that 1 dm³ = 1000 cm³.

concentration of solution

$$= \frac{2.45 \times 1000}{500} = 4.9\ g/dm^3$$

M_r of $H_2SO_4 = (2 \times 1) + 32 + (4 \times 16) = 98$

$$\text{concentration of solution} = \frac{4.9}{98}$$
$$= 0.05\ mol/dm^3$$

Worked example

Calculate the mass of sodium carbonate, Na_2CO_3, needed to make 250 cm³ of a solution that has a concentration of 0.050 mol/dm³.

Convert the concentration into g/dm³.

(relative atomic masses: C = 12, O = 16, Na = 23) **(3 marks)**

M_r of $Na_2CO_3 = (2 \times 23) + 12 + (3 \times 16) = 106$

concentration of solution = 0.050 × 106
$$= 5.3\ g/dm^3$$

$$\text{mass of solute in 250 cm}^3 = \frac{5.3 \times 250}{1000} = 1.325\ g$$

Exam practice

1. $25.0\,cm^3$ of potassium hydroxide solution was neutralised by $35.0\,cm^3$ of hydrochloric acid of concentration $0.150\,mol/dm^3$.

   $HCl + KOH \rightarrow KCl + H_2O$

   Calculate the concentration of the potassium hydroxide solution in mol/dm^3.

   You must show all of your working. **(2 marks)**

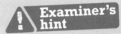

Examiner's hint

Calculate the amount (mol) of HCl, use the balanced equation to deduce the amount (mol) of KOH, then calculate the concentration of KOH.

2. $25.0\,cm^3$ of sodium hydroxide solution was neutralised by $27.5\,cm^3$ of sulfuric acid of concentration $0.050\,mol/dm^3$.

   $H_2SO_4 + 2NaOH \rightarrow Na_2SO_4 + 2H_2O$

   Calculate the concentration of the sodium hydroxide solution in g/dm^3.

   (relative atomic masses: $H = 1$, $O = 16$, $Na = 23$) **(4 marks)**

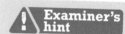

Examiner's hint

Start by calculating the amount (mol) of the solution for which you have been given the volume and concentration.

19–24,
60–66

All mole calculations

What's it all about?

You may be asked to carry out calculations from balanced equations using any combinations of masses, gas volumes and concentrations of solutions.

Worked example

Calculate the volume of hydrogen produced at rtp when excess sulfuric acid is added to 3.6 g of magnesium.

$Mg + H_2SO_4 \rightarrow MgSO_4 + H_2$

(relative atomic mass: Mg = 24; 1 mol of any gas at rtp occupies 24 dm³) **(3 marks)**

amount Mg used $= \dfrac{\text{mass in g}}{A_r}$

$= \dfrac{3.6}{24} = 0.15 \, mol$

from the balanced equation, 1 mol of Mg produces 1 mol H_2 so mol H_2 formed = mol Mg used = 0.15 mol

volume of H_2 = molar gas volume × number of moles

$= 24 × 0.15 = 3.6 \, dm^3$

Start by finding the amount (mol) of magnesium.

Use the balanced equation to deduce the amount (mol) of H_2 formed.

Now calculate the volume of H_2 formed by multiplying the amount (mol) by the volume of 1 mol of gas. Remember to include units.

Worked example

Calculate the mass of silver chloride that is formed when excess silver nitrate solution is added to 5.0 cm³ of 2.0 mol/dm³ magnesium chloride solution.

$2AgNO_3(aq) + MgCl_2(aq) \rightarrow 2AgCl(s) + Mg(NO_3)_2(aq)$

(relative atomic masses: Cl = 35.5, Ag = 108) **(3 marks)**

amount $MgCl_2$ used = concentration × $\dfrac{\text{volume in cm}^3}{1000}$

$= \dfrac{2.0 × 5.0}{1000} = 0.01 \, mol$

from the balanced equation, 1 mol of $MgCl_2$ produces 2 mol AgCl, so mol AgCl formed

$= 2 × 0.01 = 0.02 \, mol$

mass of AgCl formed = number of moles × M_r

$= 0.02(108 + 35.5)$

$= 2.87 \, g = 2.9 \, g$

Start by finding the amount of $MgCl_2$ used as that is the only substance you have data for.

Use the balanced equation to deduce the amount (mol) AgCl formed.

The best answer here is 2.9 g as the numbers in the question are given to 2 or 3 significant figures, so you should round the final answer to the **lowest** number of significant figures.

Worked example

6.00 g of calcium carbonate was added to 20.0 cm³ of 1.20 mol/dm³ hydrochloric acid.

$CaCO_3(s) + 2HCl(aq) \rightarrow CaCl_2(aq) + H_2O(l) + CO_2(g)$

(a) Show, by calculation, that calcium carbonate is in excess.

(relative atomic masses: C = 12, O = 16, Ca = 40)   **(3 marks)**

M_r of $CaCO_3 = 40 + 12 + (3 \times 16) = 100$

$$\text{amount } CaCO_3 = \frac{\text{mass in g}}{M_r} = \frac{6.00}{100} = 0.06 \text{ mol}$$

Start by calculating the amount (mol) of each substance.

$$\text{amount of HCl} = \frac{\text{concentration} \times \text{volume in cm}^3}{1000}$$

$$= \frac{1.20 \times 20.0}{1000} = 0.024 \text{ mol}$$

From the balanced equation, 1 mol $CaCO_3$ reacts with 2 mol HCl so 0.06 mol $CaCO_3$ would need 2×0.06 = 0.12 mol HCl to react with.

There is only 0.024 mol HCl so $CaCO_3$ is in excess.

Use the mole ratio from the balanced equation to deduce which substance is in excess. You could also have written that 0.024 mol of HCl needs 0.012 mol of $CaCO_3$ for reaction and there is 0.06 mol added so $CaCO_3$ is in excess.

(b) Calculate the volume of carbon dioxide formed at rtp in this experiment.

(1 mol of any gas at rtp occupies 24 000 cm³)   **(3 marks)**

From the balanced equation, 2 mol of HCl produces 1 mol CO_2

so 0.024 mol HCl will produce $\dfrac{0.024}{2}$ = 0.012 mol of CO_2

volume of CO_2 = 0.012 × 24 000 = 288 cm³

Now calculate the volume of CO_2 and remember to include the units.

Use the mole ratio from the balanced equation to deduce the amount (mol) of CO_2 produced from the amount (mol) of HCl calculated in (a).

Exam practice

1. A student heats 2.05 g of calcium nitrate, $Ca(NO_3)_2$ and collects the gas at room temperature and pressure, rtp.

$$2Ca(NO_3)_2(s) \rightarrow 2CaO(s) + 4NO_2(g) + O_2(g)$$

(a) Calculate the theoretical volume of gas that could be collected.

(relative atomic masses: N = 14, O = 16, Ca = 40; 1 mol of any gas at rtp occupies 24 000 cm³) **(3 marks)**

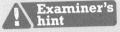

Examiner's hint

Look carefully at the equation. There are two products that are gases so you need to include both of them.

(b) The actual volume of gas collected was 675 cm³.

Calculate the percentage yield of gas produced.

(1 mark)

Make sure you explain your working. If you get the answer to (a) wrong, you can still score this mark if your working is correct.

(c) Calculate the atom economy for the production of calcium oxide, CaO, in this experiment. **(3 marks)**

Knowledge check

You need to know the equation for atom economy to answer this question.

Exam practice

2. A sample of 2.25 g of magnesium carbonate, $MgCO_3$, reacts with hydrochloric acid, HCl.

$$MgCO_3(s) + 2HCl(aq) \rightarrow MgCl_2(aq) + H_2O(l) + CO_2(g)$$

(a) Calculate the volume, in cm^3, of $2.50 \, mol/dm^3$ HCl needed to react with 2.25 g of magnesium carbonate.

Give your answer to 3 significant figures.

(relative atomic masses: C = 12, O = 16, Mg = 24)

(4 marks)

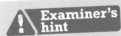

> **Examiner's hint**
>
> Start by calculating the amount (mol) of magnesium carbonate, then determine the number of moles of HCl.

(b) Calculate the volume, in cm^3, of carbon dioxide produced at rtp from 2.25 g of magnesium carbonate.

(1 mol of any gas at rtp occupies $24\,000 \, cm^3$)

(1 mark)

> Remember to give your final answer in the correct unit and the correct number of significant figures.

Electrochemistry

What's it all about?

Ionic compounds conduct electricity when molten or dissolved in water because their **ions** can move from place to place. **Electrolysis** occurs when an electric current is passed through an ionic compound and the compound decomposes.

Molten compounds always decompose into their elements.

Anode

At the positive electrode:

- ✓ anions (negative ions) are attracted
- ✓ electrons are lost
- ✓ the oxidation reaction takes place
- ✓ the non-metal forms from a molten compound
- ✓ from an aqueous solution oxygen is produced from OH^- ions **unless** the compound contains halide ions (Cl^-, Br^- or I^-). In that case the halogen is produced instead.

Cathode

At the negative electrode:

- ✓ cations (positive ions) are attracted
- ✓ electrons are gained
- ✓ the reduction reaction takes place
- ✓ metal forms from a molten compound
- ✓ hydrogen is produced, from the H^+ ions in an aqueous solution **unless** the compound contains ions from a metal less reactive than hydrogen. In that case the metal is produced instead.

Half equations

Half equations show how the ions lose or gain electrons at the electrodes to form neutral products. The number of electrons must balance the number of charges on the ions, for example

$2Cl^-(aq) \rightarrow Cl_2(g) + 2e^-$ oxidation

$2H^+(aq) + 2e^- \rightarrow H_2(g)$ reduction

Remember OIL RIG – oxidation is loss (of electrons), reduction is gain (of electrons)

Fuel cells

A cell (battery) uses chemical reactions to produce a voltage.

Chemical cell	Hydrogen–oxygen fuel cell
Uses two different metals and solutions containing their ions	Uses hydrogen and oxygen
Can be made into a battery that is portable	Needs a constant supply of gases so is not easily portable
May contain harmful or toxic substances	Produces water as the only product
Stops producing a voltage when one of the reactants is used up	

Worked example

(a) Draw a labelled diagram to show how the electrolysis of molten zinc chloride is carried out in a school laboratory. **(3 marks)**

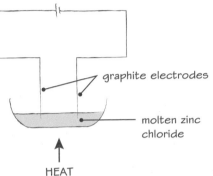

graphite electrodes

molten zinc chloride

↑
HEAT

(b) Zinc is produced at the cathode.

$$Zn^{2+}(l) + 2e^- \rightarrow Zn(l)$$

  (i) Explain why this reaction is reduction. **(2 marks)**

The zinc ions have gained two electrons.

  (ii) Write the half equation for the reaction at the anode. Include state symbols. **(2 marks)**

$$2Cl^-(l) \rightarrow Cl_2(g) + 2e^-$$

Had a go ☐   Nearly there ☐   Nailed it! ☐

Exam practice

1. In a fuel cell, hydrogen atoms form ions then the hydrogen ions react with oxygen to form water.

   $$2H_2(g) \rightarrow 4H^+(aq) + 4e^-$$

   $$4H^+(aq) + 4e^- + O_2(g) \rightarrow 2H_2O(l)$$

   Explain which of these two half equations shows oxidation. **(2 marks)**

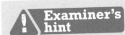

Examiner's hint

Think about OIL RIG.

2. Two separate samples of copper sulfate solution were electrolysed using copper electrodes and graphite electrodes.

   Compare and contrast the formation of the products in these two experiments. Include half equations for the reactions occurring at the electrodes. **(6 marks)**

Examiner's hint

Make sure that you know the Core Practicals.

You should include at least one similarity and one difference in these experiments.

3. An aqueous solution of sodium chloride is electrolysed using inert electrodes. The solution contains Na^+ and Cl^- ions from sodium chloride as well as H^+ and OH^- ions from water.

Two gases are produced during the electrolysis.

Explain the formation of the two gases from the ions in the solution. You may include half equations in your answer. **(6 marks)**

> **⚠ Examiner's hint**
>
> Start by working out which two gases are formed. There is only one possible gas formed at the cathode but there is a choice of two gases at the anode.

> You can either write half equations or explain what they represent in words.

Metals

What's it all about?

Displacement

A more reactive metal will **displace** a less reactive metal from its salts in solution. These are redox reactions. The atoms of the more reactive metal are oxidised by losing electrons. The cations of the less reactive metal are reduced by gaining electrons.

For example, copper displaces silver from silver nitrate solution.

$$Cu(s) + 2AgNO_3(aq) \rightarrow Cu(NO_3)_2(aq) + 2Ag(s)$$

The nitrate ions are spectator ions and are left out of the half equations as they do not change.

This can be written as two half equations.

$$Cu(s) \rightarrow Cu^{2+}(aq) + 2e^- \text{ oxidation}$$
$$2Ag^+(aq) + 2e^- \rightarrow 2Ag(s) \text{ reduction}$$

Overall ionic equation:

$$Cu(s) + 2Ag^+(aq) \rightarrow 2Ag(s) + Cu^{2+}(aq)$$

Extraction of metals from their ores

more reactive   less reactive

electrolysis   heating with carbon

⟶ carbon ⟶

- reduction: electrons gained
- energy needed for heating and electric current

- reduction: oxygen lost
- energy needed for heating and the reaction to happen

For example aluminium from aluminium oxide:

cathode: $Al^{3+} + 3e^- \rightarrow Al$
anode: $2O^{2-} \rightarrow O_2 + 4e^-$

For example iron from iron oxide:

$$Fe_2O_3 + 3C \rightarrow 2Fe + 3CO$$

Biological methods are being developed for the extraction of some metals, for example phytoextraction and bioleaching.

Corrosion

This is an oxidation reaction as the metal gains oxygen or loses electrons. Usually, the higher the metal in the **reactivity series**, the more easily its atoms lose electrons to form cations so the more rapidly it corrodes. A few metals, such as aluminium, do not corrode as they have a protective oxide layer on the surface.

Transition metals

Transition metals and their compounds are often useful as **catalysts**. These substances increase the rate of a chemical reaction **without**:

- altering the products of the reaction
- changing chemically
- changing in mass at the end of the reaction.

Worked example

(a) Zinc reacts with aqueous copper(II) sulfate. Write an ionic equation for this reaction. Include state symbols. **(2 marks)**

$Zn(s) + Cu^{2+}(aq) \rightarrow Zn^{2+}(aq) + Cu(s)$

 Leave out the ions that do not change, that is, sulfate ions.

(b) Explain, in terms of electrons, why this is a redox reaction. **(2 marks)**

Zinc atoms are oxidised as they have lost electrons to form cations. Copper ions have been reduced to copper atoms as they have gained electrons.

 Use the ionic equation to help you to work this out.

 Think carefully about which particles are involved. Some atoms are changing to ions and some ions are changing into atoms. You must use the correct terminology.

(c) A metal **X** corrodes rapidly in contact with moist air. **X** can only be extracted by electrolysis of its molten ore. **X** reacts rapidly with cold water and the gas produced ignites, giving a lilac flame.

Comment on how all of the information given can be used to identify metal **X**. **(4 marks)**

X must be high in the reactivity series as it reacts rapidly with oxygen and water and corrodes quickly.

X must be a metal between potassium and aluminium in the reactivity series as these metals can only be extracted by the electrolysis of their molten ores.

X must be potassium, sodium or calcium as these are the only metals that react rapidly with cold water.

X is potassium because it gives a lilac flame.

 'Comment on' is used as command when you are given a number of pieces of information and data. You need to write about each piece of information and come to a judgement. Questions using this command are worth at least 4 marks, so you need to use all of the information in the question.

Take each piece of information in turn and state what you can work out from it.

 Don't forget to include the identity of the metal in your answer.

Exam practice

1. Sodium is in group 1 of the periodic table and iron is a transition metal.

Give **one** difference in their physical properties and **one** difference in their chemical properties. **(2 marks)**

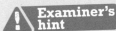
Make sure that you can answer all the straightforward questions like this one.

2. A ship's hull is made from steel. Explain why attaching a piece of magnesium to the ship's hull prevents it from rusting. Include a half equation in your answer. **(3 marks)**

Examiner's hint

Think about the relative reactivities of magnesium and steel (iron).

Knowledge check

Remember that half equations involve two species of one substance and they contain electrons.

3. Explain why a gold alloy is stronger than pure gold. **(4 marks)**

Knowledge check

Think about the arrangement of particles.

Exam practice

4. Magnesium occurs as magnesium chloride and iron occurs as iron oxide in the Earth's crust. These metals are extracted from their ores by different methods.

   Explain, in terms of the position of these metals in the reactivity series and the amount of energy used in the extraction processes, why magnesium and iron are extracted by different methods. **(6 marks)**

You are not expected to know the details of the extraction of magnesium but you should be able to predict this from its position in the reactivity series.

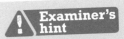
Examiner's hint

Look carefully at the section between the commas in the second paragraph of the question.
Your explanation must refer to these two points to get a good mark.

67–69, 71

Reversible reactions and equilibria

What's it all about?

Reversible reactions

When a reversible reaction takes place in a closed system, such as a stoppered flask, it can reach equilibrium. All chemical equilibria are **dynamic** equilibria as the forward and backward reactions are still happening. When a reaction reaches dynamic equilibrium:

- the forwards and backwards reactions occur at the same rate
- the concentrations of the reactants and products do not change.

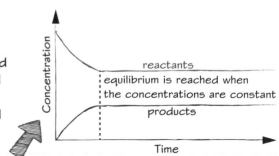

The concentrations of reactants and products are **not** the same. The concentration of products could be higher than the concentration of reactants.

Equilibrium

The position of an equilibrium and how fast equilibrium is attained depend on the conditions.

Change in conditions	Effect on equilibrium position	Effect on rate of reaching equilibrium
temperature increased	moves in the direction of the endothermic reaction	rate increased
pressure increased	moves in the direction of the fewest molecules of gas	rate increased (if reacting gases are present)
concentration of a reacting substance increased	moves in the direction away from the reacting substance	rate increased
catalyst added	no change	rate increased

Industrial processes

1 Many involve at least one reversible reaction.

2 Temperature and pressure are chosen to ensure an acceptable yield in an acceptable time. Often, these conditions are a compromise.

3 A suitable catalyst will increase the rate of reaction, allowing a lower temperature and reducing the cost as less energy will be needed.

4 Usually do not allow reactions to reach equilibrium as the product is removed as it forms.

5 Any unreacted substances are recycled through the industrial plant.

Worked example

In which of the following reactions will a change in pressure have no effect on the equilibrium yield of the product?

(1 mark)

☐ **A** $2NO_2(g) \rightleftharpoons N_2O_4(g)$

☒ **B** $H_2(g) + I_2(g) \rightleftharpoons 2HI(g)$

☐ **C** $2NO(g) + O_2(g) \rightleftharpoons 2NO_2(g)$

☐ **D** $N_2(g) + 3H_2(g) \rightleftharpoons 2NH_3(g)$

A change in pressure only affects an equilibrium in which there is a change in the number of gas molecules.

This is the correct answer as there are 2 moles of gas on the left of the equation and 2 moles on the right. There is a change in the number of moles of gas in all the other answers.

Worked example

Explain the effect, if any, of increasing the pressure on the equilibrium yield of NO in this reaction.

$4NH_3(g) + 5O_2(g) \rightleftharpoons 4NO(g) + 6H_2O(g)$

(2 marks)

The yield of NO decreases because the increase in pressure favours the reaction in which there is a decrease in the total number of moles of **gas** molecules.

The yield may increase, decrease or stay the same.

There are 9 moles of **gas** on the left of the equation and 10 moles of **gas** on the right.

Worked example

The reaction of sulfur dioxide with oxygen to form sulfur trioxide is exothermic.

$2SO_2(g) + O_2(g) \rightleftharpoons 2SO_3(g)$

The temperature used is 450 °C.

Explain the effect, if any, on the equilibrium yield of sulfur trioxide if a temperature higher than 450 °C is used.

(3 marks)

A higher temperature favours the endothermic reaction. In this case, this is the backwards reaction, so the equilibrium yield of SO_3 decreases.

Being exothermic is important as it affects the equilibrium yield when the temperature is changed.

You must state which reaction is endothermic.

Exam practice

1. The gases dinitrogen tetroxide (N_2O_4) and nitrogen dioxide (NO_2) form an equilibrium mixture at room temperature. The forward reaction is endothermic.

$$N_2O_4(g) \rightleftharpoons 2NO_2(g)$$

   colourless   brown

Predict how the appearance of the equilibrium mixture will change when the temperature increases.

Justify your answer.   **(3 marks)**

Examiner's hint

When describing a colour change, give the starting colour as well as the end colour.

You must give reasons for your answer.

2. Potassium chromate solution is yellow and contains chromate ions, CrO_4^{2-}. Chromate ions exist in the following equilibrium.

$$2CrO_4^{2-}(aq) + 2H^+(aq) \rightleftharpoons Cr_2O_7^{2-}(aq) + H_2O(l)$$

   yellow   orange

Predict how the appearance of the equilibrium mixture will change when dilute sulfuric acid is added.

Justify your answer.   **(3 marks)**

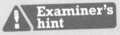

Examiner's hint

Think about the ion that is present in all dilute acids.

Exam practice

3. One of the stages in the production of sulfuric acid involves the oxidation of sulfur dioxide to sulfur trioxide. The reaction is exothermic.

$$2SO_2(g) + O_2(g) \rightleftharpoons 2SO_3(g)$$

The conditions used in one industrial process are: 400 °C, a pressure of 2 atmospheres and a catalyst.

It is proposed to change the conditions to 600 °C and a pressure of 10 atmospheres while keeping the same catalyst.

Predict the effects of the changes in temperature and pressure on the rate of reaction and the equilibrium yield of sulfur trioxide. Justify your answers. **(6 marks)**

Examiner's hint

You are not expected to know any details about this process but you should be able to apply your knowledge of the effects of changing temperature and pressure to any equilibrium.

Synoptic link

To answer this question you will need to use the factors that affect the rate of a reaction.

Your answer must give reasons for the changes in rate of reaction and equilibrium yield of SO_3.

72–77

Groups in the periodic table

What's it all about?

Comparison of the alkali metals, the halogens and noble gases

Group 1 (alkali metals)	Group 7 (halogens)	Group O (noble gases)
✓ All metals	✓ All non-metals	✓ All non-metals
✓ Metallic bonding	✓ Diatomic molecules with a covalent bond between the atoms. Weak forces between the molecules.	✓ Very weak forces between the separate atoms.
✓ Solids with relatively low melting points.	✓ Change from gas to liquid to solid down the group as the melting and boiling points increase due to increasing strength of intermolecular forces.	✓ All are gases at room temperature. The boiling points increase down the group as the strength of the intermolecular forces increases.
✓ Only form ionic compounds, as the alkali metals form ions with only one positive charge.	✓ Form ionic compounds as the halogens form halide ions with one negative charge. They can also form covalent compounds, e.g. hydrogen chloride.	✓ Do not form ionic or covalent compounds.
✓ Reactivity increases down the group as: • the atoms get larger • less energy is needed to overcome the force of attraction between the nucleus and outer electron • so the outer electron is more easily lost. ✓ React with non-metals to form salts.	✓ Reactivity decreases down the group as: • the atoms get larger • the attraction between the nucleus and incoming electron decreases • so an additional electron is less easily gained.	✓ Unreactive as the atoms have full outer shells of electrons and they have no tendency to gain, lose or share electrons.

Worked example

When an aqueous solution of chlorine is added to potassium bromide solution, the solution turns orange. Explain this observation. Include an ionic equation in your answer. State symbols are not required. **(3 marks)**

Chlorine is more reactive than bromine so it oxidises bromide ions to bromine or chlorine displaces bromine from potassium bromide. The orange colour is due to bromine

$Cl_2 + 2Br^- \rightarrow 2Cl^- + Br_2$

> You need to identify what has caused the orange colour and explain how it has been formed.

> There are only three possible ionic equations for the displacement reactions of halogens and they all follow the same pattern so learn them.

Worked example

Chlorine reacts with hot aluminium to form solid aluminium chloride, $AlCl_3$.

(a) Write the balanced equation for this reaction. Include state symbols. **(2 marks)**

$2Al(s) + 3Cl_2(g) \rightarrow 2AlCl_3(s)$

(b) Explain, in terms of electrons, why this is a redox reaction. **(4 marks)**

Aluminium atoms lose electrons to form aluminium ions : $Al \rightarrow Al^{3+} + 3e^-$

So aluminium is oxidised.

Chlorine atoms gain electrons to form chloride ions : $Cl_2 + 2e^- \rightarrow 2Cl^-$

So chlorine is reduced.

> All halogens react with metals to form salts.

> The formula of aluminium chloride and its state are given in the question.

> It is acceptable to give the correct half equations, and to state which one shows oxidation and which one shows reduction.

Worked example

Sodium reacts with cold water to form hydrogen and sodium hydroxide solution.

Explain, in terms of electronic configurations, what happens to a sodium atom when it reacts to form a sodium ion in sodium hydroxide. **(2 marks)**

Na is 2.8.1, Na+ is 2.8

A sodium atom loses an electron to form a sodium ion (so it is oxidised).

> All of the alkali metals react with cold water to form hydrogen and a metal hydroxide (alkaline solution).

> There is no need to add a balancing number if it is a 1.

Exam practice

1. A student carries out experiments to determine the order of reactivity of the three halogens: bromine, chlorine and iodine.

   The student is provided with aqueous solutions of the following three substances: bromine water, potassium chloride and potassium iodide.

   Describe the experiments to determine the order of reactivity. Include an explanation of how the expected observations are used to determine the order of reactivity.

   (6 marks)

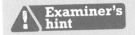

⚠ **Examiner's hint**

The best way to work out order of reactivity is to carry out displacement reactions.

It is important that you **only** use the three solutions provided.

Don't forget to include the observations you expect from the experiments and how they can be used.

Exam practice

2. Compare and contrast the trends in reactivity of the elements in group 1 and group 7 of the periodic table.

   Include an explanation of the trends.   **(6 marks)**

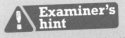

Examiner's hint

Write about similarities and differences.

Knowledge check

Remember that each atom only has one outer shell.

REVISION GUIDE Chemistry | 78–80, 110

Rates of reaction

What's it all about?

Rate and time

A reaction that takes a long time has a low rate of reaction whereas a reaction that occurs in a short time has a high rate of reaction. The rate of reaction is inversely proportional to the time taken.

$$\text{rate} \propto \frac{1}{\text{time}}$$

Factors affecting rate of reaction

	Increase in temperature	Increase in concentration or pressure	Increase in surface area : volume ratio
Particles	particles have more energy and move faster	more particles in the same volume of solution or gas	more particles of solid reactant available on surface to react
Frequency of collisions	increases	increases	increases
Energy of collisions	increases	stays the same	stays the same

Nanoparticles have very large surface area : volume ratios and many are good catalysts.

Calculating the rate of a reaction

The rate of a reaction at any time is calculated by drawing a graph of quantity changing with time, for example the volume of a gas. Then draw a tangent to a curve at that time and calculate the gradient.

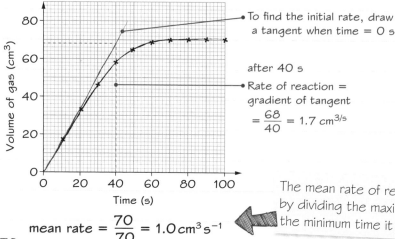

To find the initial rate, draw a tangent when time = 0 s

after 40 s

Rate of reaction = gradient of tangent

$$= \frac{68}{40} = 1.7 \text{ cm}^3/\text{s}$$

The mean rate of reaction is calculated by dividing the maximum volume of gas by the minimum time it takes to form.

$$\text{mean rate} = \frac{70}{70} = 1.0 \text{ cm}^3\,\text{s}^{-1}$$

Worked example

A catalytic converter is used in a car exhaust system to speed up the conversion of carbon monoxide and unburnt hydrocarbons into carbon dioxide and water. The catalytic converter contains a honeycomb structure covered with a thin layer of the catalyst.

Explain why the catalyst is spread onto the honeycomb structure rather than used as large pieces. **(3 marks)**

The thin layer of catalyst has a larger surface area : volume ratio (than the large pieces) so there are more particles of solid available on the surface.

The frequency of collisions between the gases and catalyst increases so the reaction is faster.

Don't just state that the catalyst has a larger surface area. Always refer to the surface area : volume ratio.

Don't just state that there are 'more collisions'. It is the frequency of collisions that is important.

Worked example

Dilute hydrochloric acid was added to excess magnesium to produce hydrogen and magnesium chloride. The volume of hydrogen was measured at regular time intervals. The results were plotted on a graph.

Sketch a line on the graph to show the results you would expect if the experiment was repeated using hydrochloric acid of half the concentration, keeping all other conditions the same. **(2 marks)**

Think about the rate of reaction (the steepness of the line) and the volume of gas produced (where the line levels off).

Half the concentration of acid gives a lower rate of reaction so the line is less steep at the start.

There will be half the number of particles in the acid with half the concentration so only half as much hydrogen is produced.

Volume of gas / Time

Exam practice

1. Calcium carbonate reacts with dilute hydrochloric acid.

$$CaCO_3(s) + 2HCl(aq) \rightarrow CaCl_2(aq) + H_2O(l) + CO_2(g)$$

6.0 g of large pieces of calcium carbonate are placed in a conical flask and 50 cm³ of 0.2 mol/dm³ hydrochloric acid is added. The carbon dioxide is collected in a gas syringe and the volume is measured.

The results are shown in the table.

Time (s)	Volume of CO_2 (cm³)
0	0
30	36
60	60
90	72
120	74
150	74

(a) Plot a graph of these results on a piece of graph paper. **(3 marks)**

(b) (i) Draw a tangent to the curve when time = 0. **(1 mark)**

　　(ii) Use the tangent to calculate the initial rate of reaction. Include units in your answer. **(3 marks)**

(c) Sketch a line on your graph to show the results you would expect if the experiment were carried out using 6 g of powdered calcium carbonate, keeping all other conditions the same. **(2 marks)**

(d) Use the amounts of calcium carbonate and hydrochloric acid given and the balanced equation to calculate which reactant is in excess. **(3 marks)**

Maths skills

Choose a suitable scale so that the points cover at least half of the axes and with simple increments such as 5 or 10. Label the axes, including units.

Maths skills

The tangent is a straight line just touching the curve at one point only. In this question it must touch the curve when time = 0.

Maths skills

Find the gradient of the tangent. Gradient

$$= \frac{increase\ in\ y}{increase\ in\ x}$$

Examiner's hint

Consider the rate of reaction and the volume of gas given off.

Synoptic link

Start by calculating the amount, in mol, of each reactant, then use the balanced equation.

Exam practice

2. Magnesium ribbon reacts with dilute sulfuric acid.

$$Mg(s) + H_2SO_4(aq) \rightarrow MgSO_4(aq) + H_2(g)$$

The time was found for a 2 cm length of magnesium ribbon to completely react with the sulfuric acid.

The experiment was repeated at different temperatures and using different concentrations of sulfuric acid, keeping all other conditions the same.

Examiner's hint

You must refer to the results of these experiments by quoting the experiment numbers and specific data from them.

The results are shown in the table.

	Experiment 1	Experiment 2	Experiment 3
Concentration of H_2SO_4 in mol/dm³	0.1	0.05	0.05
Temperature in °C	20	20	40
Time taken for magnesium to react in s	45	90	23

Your answer must refer to both particles and collisions.

Explain, in terms of particles and collisions, the effect of changing the concentration of sulfuric acid and the effect of changing the temperature on the rate of this reaction.

Refer to the results of the experiments in your answer.

(6 marks)

Don't forget to explain the effect of changing **concentration** and changing the **temperature**.

Continue your answer on a separate piece of paper if necessary.

Heat energy changes

What's it all about?

Exothermic and endothermic reactions

In an exothermic reaction:

✓ the temperature of the reaction mixture or surroundings increases

✓ heat energy is given out

✓ more energy is given out when bonds are made in the products than is needed to break bonds in the reactants.

For example, neutralisation and displacement reactions.

In an endothermic reaction:

✓ the temperature of the reaction mixture or surroundings decreases

✓ heat energy is taken in

✓ more energy is needed to break bonds in the reactants than is given out when bonds are made in the products.

For example, thermal decomposition and cracking.

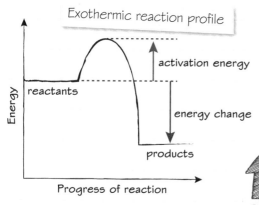

Exothermic reaction profile

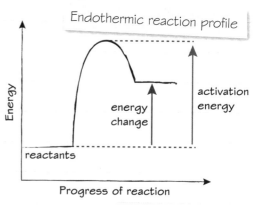

Endothermic reaction profile

Some reactions, for example dissolving and precipitation, can be exothermic or endothermic.

Bond energies

All covalent bonds have different bond energies. You will be given the values in the exam paper, if you need them.

The bond energy is:

• the energy needed to break 1 mol of a particular covalent bond

• measured in $kJ\,mol^{-1}$.

In a chemical reaction, some bonds are broken and some bonds are made.

For example, the bond energy of an O-H bond is $464\,kJ\,mol^{-1}$ so $464\,kJ$ is needed to break 1 mol of O-H bonds and $464\,kJ$ is given out when 1 mol of O-H bonds is made.

Energy = Energy − Energy
change   needed to   released
          break bonds when bonds
                       are made

Worked example

The reaction profile for a reaction is shown here.

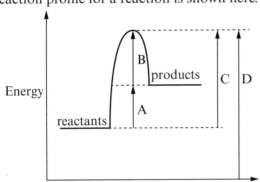

(a) Which letter, A, B, C or D, shows the activation energy of this reaction? **(1 mark)**

C

(b) Give a reason why this reaction profile shows that this is an endothermic reaction. **(1 mark)**

The energy level of the products is higher than that of the reactants.

> The activation energy is the energy the reactants need to react so must start at the energy level of the reactants.

> A is the energy change for the reaction, B would be the activation energy if the reaction were going in the reverse direction and D cannot be correct as it is starting from the x axis with an energy of 0.

> Don't just state that 'energy is taken in', refer to the diagram in your answer.

Worked example

Ethene reacts with hydrogen to form ethane.

$$\underset{H}{\overset{H}{\diagdown}}C=C\underset{H}{\overset{H}{\diagup}} \quad + \quad H-H \quad \rightarrow \quad H-\underset{\underset{H}{|}}{\overset{\overset{H}{|}}{C}}-\underset{\underset{H}{|}}{\overset{\overset{H}{|}}{C}}-H$$

Calculate the energy change for this reaction. **(4 marks)**

Bond energies (in kJ mol^{-1}): C–H = 413, C=C = 612, C–C = 348, H–H = 436

Bonds broken: Bonds made:

C=C 612   C–C 348

H–H 436   2 C–H 2 × 413

Total 1048   Total 1174

Energy change = bonds broken – bonds made

$\qquad$ = $\quad$ 1048 $\quad$ – $\quad$ 1174

$\qquad$ = –126 kJ mol^{-1}

> You could also include the 4C–H bonds but you need to remember to remake them.

> The C=C must be broken before the C–C bond forms.

> You must include the sign with the answer or state that the reaction is exothermic.

Exam practice

1. Ethanol burns completely in oxygen.

$$H-\underset{\underset{H}{|}}{\overset{\overset{H}{|}}{C}}-\underset{\underset{H}{|}}{\overset{\overset{H}{|}}{C}}-O-H \ + \ 3\,O{=}O \ \rightarrow \ 2\,O{=}C{=}O \ + \ 3\,H-O-H$$

(a) Calculate the energy change for this reaction.

(Bond energies (in kJ mol⁻¹): C–C = 347, C–H = 413, C–O = 358, O=O = 498, C=O = 805, O–H = 464)

(4 marks)

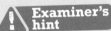
Examiner's hint

Look carefully to see how many bonds of each type are broken and made. Don't forget that there are 2 O–H bonds in each water molecule.

Remember to include a sign in your answer. This is a combustion reaction so you should know whether it is exothermic or endothermic.

(b) Complete the reaction profile for the combustion of ethanol.

Include labels for the energy of the products, the activation energy and the energy change.   **(3 marks)**

This is a sketch and not an accurately plotted graph.

Heat
Energy | reactants
_____

Progress of reaction

Examiner's hint

Check to make sure that you have included all labels. Use the sign of the energy change you calculated in (a) to decide whether the reaction is exothermic or endothermic.

2. A student wrote the following plan to investigate comparing the combustion of ethanol and propanol.

- Record the mass of the ethanol burner and cap.
- Add $100\,cm^3$ of water to a beaker.
- Clamp the beaker of water above the ethanol burner.
- Remove the cap of the ethanol burner and light the ethanol.
- Allow the water to heat up by about $20\,°C$.
- Blow out the flame and reweigh the ethanol burner.
- Repeat the experiment with the propanol burner.

(a) State **three** improvements to the plan.　　(3 marks)

> **Practical skills**
>
> This plan is based on a Core Practical. Use your knowledge of the Core Practical to help you to answer the questions.

> **Examiner's hint**
>
> Think about the important things that the student has left out of the plan.

(b) State **three** factors that need to be controlled when the experiment is repeated with propanol.　(3 marks)

> For (b) these are the factors that need to be controlled to make sure more than one variable does not affect the experiment.

(c) Some results of an investigation are shown here.

Alcohol	Ethanol	Propanol
Formula	C_2H_5OH	C_3H_7OH
Initial mass of burner + cap (g)	156.64	163.20
Final mass of burner + cap (g)	155.82	162.81
Initial temp of $100\,cm^3$ of water (°C)	20	20
Final temp of $100\,cm^3$ of water (°C)	41	39
Temp rise per g		
Temp rise per mol		

> The temperature rise per g is the mass of alcohol burnt.

> To calculate the temperature rise per mol, start by using the formulae given in the table and the relative atomic masses from a periodic table to calculate the relative formula mass of each alcohol.

Complete the missing values in the table. Give your answers to an appropriate number of significant figures.　(4 marks)

Hydrocarbons

What's it all about?

A **hydrocarbon** is a compound that contains carbon and hydrogen atoms only. C_2H_6O is not a hydrocarbon as it also contains an oxygen atom. Alkanes and alkenes are two homologous series of hydrocarbons.

How alkenes and alkanes are similar.

👍 Boiling points of both homologous series increase as the number of carbon atoms increases because:

- the intermolecular forces are stronger
- more energy is needed to overcome them.

👍 Both undergo complete combustion to produce carbon dioxide and water.

👍 Both undergo incomplete combustion to produce water, carbon and carbon monoxide.

How alkenes and alkanes are different.

	Alkanes	Alkenes
General formula	C_nH_{2n+2}	C_nH_{2n}
Example	Ethane $H-\overset{\overset{H}{\|}}{C}-\overset{\overset{H}{\|}}{C}-H$ $\underset{H}{\|}$ $\underset{H}{\|}$	Ethene $\underset{H}{\overset{H}{>}}C=C\underset{H}{\overset{H}{<}}$
Bonding and saturation	Only single covalent bonds so molecules are saturated	Single covalent bonds and a C=C double bond so molecules are unsaturated
Polymerisation	Cannot form polymers	Can form addition polymers
Reaction with bromine water	No reaction – bromine water stays orange	An addition reaction occurs – bromine water changes from orange to colourless $\underset{H}{\overset{H}{>}}C=C\underset{H}{\overset{H}{<}} + Br_2 \longrightarrow H-\overset{\overset{H}{\|}}{\underset{\underset{Br}{\|}}{C}}-\overset{\overset{H}{\|}}{\underset{\underset{Br}{\|}}{C}}-H$

Worked example

An alkene has a relative formula mass of 70.

Deduce the molecular formula of this alkene. **(2 marks)**

General formula of an alkene is C_nH_{2n} and the M_r of CH_2 is
$$12 + (2 \times 1) = 14$$
$$\frac{70}{14} = 5$$
So the alkene is C_5H_{10}

The relative formula mass of all alkenes is a multiple of 14.

Worked example

Write the balanced equation for the complete combustion of heptane, C_7H_{16}. **(2 marks)**

$$C_7H_{16} + 11O_2 \rightarrow 7CO_2 + 8H_2O$$

1. Write the formulae of the reactants and products
2. Number of CO_2 = number of C in alkane
3. Number of H_2O = half the number of H in alkane
4. Number of O_2 = half the number of O atoms in CO_2 and H_2O

Worked example

During a cracking reaction, each molecule of an alkane with the formula $C_{10}H_{22}$ formed two molecules of ethene, C_2H_4, and one molecule of another hydrocarbon **A**.

Deduce the molecular formula of hydrocarbon **A**. **(1 mark)**

$$C_{10}H_{22} \rightarrow 2C_2H_4 + A$$
A is C_6H_{14}

Cracking is a thermal decomposition reaction so nothing is added to the hydrocarbon, it just breaks up.

You should use the fact that two molecules of ethene are formed to work out your answer.

It is easiest to answer this question by showing the information given as a balanced equation.
$$C = 10 - (2 \times 2) = 6$$
$$H = 22 - (2 \times 4) = 14$$

Exam practice

1. Cycloalkanes are saturated hydrocarbons in which the carbon atoms are joined in a ring.

   The table shows the name, formulae and structures of some cycloalkanes.

Name	Formula	Structure
cyclopropane		
cyclobutane	C_4H_8	
cyclopentane		

Examiner's hint

Use the information given to deduce the missing name, formulae and structures of the cycloalkanes.

   (a) Deduce the formulae of cyclopropane and cyclopentane and draw the structure of cyclobutane. **(3 marks)**

   (b) Deduce the formula of the cycloalkane with 7 carbon atoms. Justify your answer. **(2 marks)**

   You must give a reason for your answer.

   (c) Write the balanced equation for the complete combustion of C_4H_8. **(2 marks)**

   All hydrocarbons give the same products during complete combustion.

Exam practice

2. A hydrocarbon contains 82.8% carbon. The relative formula mass of this hydrocarbon is 58.

(a) (i) Calculate the empirical formula of this hydrocarbon. **(3 marks)**

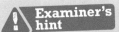

Assume you have 100 g of the compound so 82.8 g is carbon and you can calculate the mass of hydrogen since this is a hydrocarbon.

(ii) Deduce the molecular formula of this hydrocarbon. **(2 marks)**

Calculate the empirical formula first then use the M_r to deduce the molecular formula.

(b) Draw the structure of this hydrocarbon, showing all of the bonds. **(1 mark)**

3. The relative formula mass of a hydrocarbon is 84. The hydrocarbon reacts with bromine to form a colourless liquid.

Deduce the structure of this hydrocarbon. Justify your answer and include an equation for the reaction, using molecular formulae. **(4 marks)**

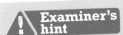

You must give reasons for your answer.

Alcohols and carboxylic acids

What's it all about?

	Alcohols	Carboxylic acids
General formula	$C_nH_{2n+1}OH$	$C_nH_{2n+1}COOH$
Functional group	$-OH$	$-COOH$
Acidity	These form neutral solutions.	These are weak acids so solutions turn indicators into their acid colour, for example blue litmus turns red.
Reactions	• Burn to produce carbon dioxide and water • Are oxidised to produce carboxylic acids • Are dehydrated to produce alkenes	• Burn to produce carbon dioxide and water • React with magnesium to form a salt and hydrogen • React with a metal carbonate to form a salt, water and carbon dioxide • React with alkalis and bases to form a salt and water

Examples of reaction equations

1   Burning alcohols

$$C_2H_5OH + 3O_2 \rightarrow 2CO_2 + 3H_2O$$

Take care when balancing these equations as there is an oxygen atom in the alcohol molecule.

2   Dehydrating alcohols

$$C_2H_5OH \rightarrow C_2H_4 + H_2O$$

Dehydration is the chemical removal of water from a substance. A dehydrating agent, such as heated aluminium oxide, is used for this but it does not change as it is a catalyst so is not included in the equation. Ethanol is dehydrated to form ethene.

3   Carboxylic acids and magnesium

$$2CH_3COOH + Mg \rightarrow Mg(CH_3COO)_2 + H_2$$

The salt formed from ethanoic acid is called magnesium ethanoate.

4   Carboxylic acids and metal carbonates

$$2CH_3COOH + Na_2CO_3 \rightarrow 2NaCH_3COO + H_2O + CO_2$$

5   Carboxylic acids and alkalis

$$CH_3COOH + NaOH \rightarrow NaCH_3COO + H_2O$$

The formulae of the salts can also be written as $(CH_3COO)_2Mg$ and CH_3COONa

Worked example

Pentanol is a liquid and its molecules have the formula $C_5H_{11}OH$.

(a) Explain how you know that pentanol is a member of the alcohol homologous series.

(2 marks)

Its formula agrees with the general formula for alcohols of $C_nH_{2n+1}OH$ and all alcohols contain the functional group –OH.

You are only expected to know the names and formulae of the first four members of the alcohols but you should be able to make predictions about other members with more carbon atoms.

(b) Predict the structure of a molecule of pentanol, showing all of the covalent bonds. **(2 marks)**

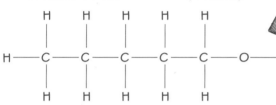

Show the OH group at the end of the carbon chain and don't forget the O–H bond.

(c) Write the balanced equation for the complete combustion of pentanol, $C_5H_{11}OH$. Include state symbols.

(3 marks)

$$C_5H_{11}OH(l) + 7\tfrac{1}{2}O_2(g) \rightarrow 5CO_2(g) + 6H_2O(l)$$

Start by balancing the carbon atoms, then the hydrogen atoms and finally the oxygen atoms. Don't forget to include the oxygen atom in pentanol.

The physical state of pentanol is given in the first line of the question.

You could also double the balancing numbers to give $2C_5H_{11}OH(l) + 15O_2(g) \rightarrow 10CO_2(g) + 12H_2O(l)$

(d) Give the name of the organic product formed when pentanol is dehydrated. **(1 mark)**

pentene

Ethanol is dehydrated to form ethene so pentanol will form pentene when it is dehydrated.

Exam practice

1. Complete the table to show the names, formulae and structures of some alcohols and carboxylic acids.

(4 marks)

Show all of the covalent bonds in the structures.

Name	Formula	Structure
	C_2H_5OH	
propanol		
		H—C=O, O—H (H—C with double bond to O and single bond to O—H)
	C_3H_7COOH	

2. An aqueous solution of ethanoic acid, CH_3COOH, reacts with calcium carbonate to form a soluble salt and one other product.

   (a) Give **one** observation made during this reaction.

   (1 mark)

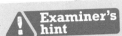

Examiner's hint

Write down what you would **see** if you carried out this experiment. Don't write down the names of any products.

   (b) Write the balanced equation for this reaction. Include state symbols. **(3 marks)**

Synoptic link

A calcium ion is Ca^{2+} and an ethanoate ion is CH_3COO^-.

The introduction to the question will help you with two of the state symbols.

Exam practice

3. A sample of an organic compound, **A**, contained 1.44 g of carbon, 0.32 g of hydrogen and 0.64 g of oxygen. The relative formula mass of **A** is 60.

   A can be oxidised to form an organic compound, **B**. An aqueous solution of **B** reacts with magnesium to produce hydrogen and a soluble salt.

   (a) Calculate the molecular formula of **A**.   **(4 marks)**

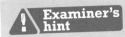

⚠ **Examiner's hint**

Start by calculating the empirical formula and molecular formula of **A**.

   (b) Identify compounds **A** and **B**. Justify your answers.
   (4 marks)

You must give reasons for your answers. Use the reactions to explain which functional groups are present.

   (c) Write a balanced equation for the reaction of **B** with magnesium. Include state symbols.   **(3 marks)**

Polymerisation

What's it all about?

Polymerisation occurs when a large number of small molecules (**monomers**) join together to form a long chain molecule called a **polymer**.

	Addition polymerisation	Condensation polymerisation
Monomers	Alkenes only	Diols and dicarboxylic acids
Formation	Monomers add on to each other and no small molecules are eliminated.	Monomers join together with the elimination of a small molecule, usually water. One molecule of water is formed from each ester link.
Polymer	The polymer will just have single bonds in the chain. There will not be –C=C– in the chain.	A polyester will contain an ester link. $$\overset{\displaystyle O}{\underset{\displaystyle \parallel}{}}$$ —C—O—
Example of a repeating unit	poly(propene) H CH$_3$ | | —C — C— | | H H	A **polyester**

The repeating units may be shown with brackets through the extension bonds. The atoms in the chain of the polyester may be drawn in a straight line.

Worked example

The monomers must have a functional group at each end of the molecule.

Draw the structures of the two monomers that form this polyester.

(2 marks)

It would be acceptable to draw H—O—C—C—O—H in a straight line in the dicarboxylic acid.

Exam practice

1. A polyester has the following repeating unit.

$$-\text{O}-\overset{\overset{\displaystyle H}{|}}{\underset{\underset{\displaystyle H}{|}}{\text{C}}}-\text{C}\overset{\displaystyle O}{\underset{\displaystyle O-}{}}$$

A polyester can be shown with the alcohol and the carboxylic acid groups on either end of the repeating unit.

This polyester is made from **one** monomer that contains two different functional groups.

Draw the structure of this monomer, showing all of the covalent bonds. **(2 marks)**

Examiner's hint

You will need to apply your knowledge of polyesters to this question. Think about the functional groups that react together to form an ester link.

2. An addition polymer is formed from the following monomer.

$$\overset{\displaystyle H}{\underset{\displaystyle H}{}}\text{C}=\text{C}\overset{\displaystyle CH_3}{\underset{\displaystyle CH_3}{}}$$

Examiner's hint

Apply your knowledge of addition polymerisation to this question.

Draw a section of the polymer chain, showing **two** repeating units. **(2 marks)**

Remember that there will not be a double bond in the carbon chain. There should be two repeating units in your answer, so four carbon atoms in the chain.

95–98

Qualitative analysis

What's it all about?

Ionic equations

1 Metal cations with aqueous hydroxide ions, e.g.

$$Cu^{2+}(aq) + 2OH^-(aq) \rightarrow Cu(OH)_2(s)$$

2 Ammonium ions with aqueous hydroxide ions, e.g.

$$NH_4^+(aq) + OH^-(aq) \rightarrow NH_3(g) + H_2O(l)$$

This test also works by warming solid ammonium compounds with aqueous sodium hydroxide.

3 Halide ions with aqueous silver ions, e.g.

$$Ag^+(aq) + Cl^-(aq) \rightarrow AgCl(s)$$

4 Sulfate ions with aqueous barium ions, e.g.

$$Ba^{2+}(aq) + SO_4^{2-}(aq) \rightarrow BaSO_4(s)$$

5 Carbonate ions with dilute acids, e.g.

$$CuCO_3(s) + 2H^+(aq) \rightarrow Cu^{2+}(aq) + CO_2(g) + H_2O(l)$$

This test also works with carbonate ions in solution.

Worked example

Aqueous solutions of aluminium ions and calcium ions both form white precipitates when aqueous sodium hydroxide is added to them.

(a) Describe how to distinguish between the two white precipitates. **(2 marks)**

Add excess sodium hydroxide to both precipitates.

The aluminium hydroxide precipitate will dissolve in excess sodium hydroxide but the calcium hydroxide precipitate will not.

(b) Write ionic equations for the formation of the two white precipitates. Include state symbols. **(2 marks)**

$$Al^{3+}(aq) + 3OH^-(aq) \rightarrow Al(OH)_3(s)$$
$$Ca^{2+}(aq) + 2OH^-(aq) \rightarrow Ca(OH)_2(s)$$

Notice that there are 2 marks for this question. You need to describe what needs to be added and what you would see.

The number of hydroxide ions is equal to the charge on the metal cation.

Exam practice

Solid **A** contains two different cations and one anion.
Three tests were carried out on separate portions of **A**.

Test	Observation	Conclusion
Test 1 Carry out a flame test on **A**.	A lilac flame is seen	The formula of the cation identified by this test is ....
Test 2 Add aqueous sodium hydroxide to **A** and warm the mixture.	A gas is given off that turns damp red litmus blue	The name of the gas is .... The formula of the cation identified by this test is ....
Test 3 Add a few drops of dilute hydrochloric acid to an aqueous solution of **A**, then add a few drops of aqueous barium chloride.	A white precipitate forms	The name of the white precipitate is .... The formula of the anion is ....

(a) Complete the table. **(5 marks)**

(b) Use the formulae of the ions to suggest an overall formula for **A**. **(1 mark)**

(c) (i) Explain why dilute hydrochloric is added in **Test 3**. **(2 marks)**

   (ii) Explain why dilute sulfuric acid could not be used in **Test 3**. **(2 marks)**

> **Examiner's hint**
> Check carefully to see whether you have been asked to give the name or the formula in each test.

> **A** contains two different cations and one anion. Combine the ions so there is no overall charge.

Answers

2–5. Knowledge check

1. D
2. C
3. atomic number / number of protons
4. A
5. potassium chlorate
6. C
7. D
8. D
9. B
10. 98
11. CH_2O
12. C
13. D
14. B
15. B
16. D
17. A
18. B
19. D
20. B
21. A
22. A
23. A
24. D
25. A
26. A
27. $0.00500 / 5.00 \times 10^{-3}$ mol
28. 62.5% / 63%
29. C
30. C
31. The greater the rate of reaction the lower the reaction time.
32. D
33. A
34. D
35. C
36. C

6–7. Formulae and equations

1. (a) Na_2SO_4 **(1)**
   (b) $Mg(OH)_2$ **(1)**
   (c) $Al(NO_3)_3$ **(1)**
2. (a) $2Na + 2H_2O \rightarrow 2NaOH + H_2$ **(1)**
   (b) $2Fe + 3Cl_2 \rightarrow 2FeCl_3$ **(1)**
   (c) $2C_2H_6 + 7O_2 \rightarrow 4CO_2 + 6H_2O$ or
   $C_2H_6 + 3\frac{1}{2}O_2 \rightarrow 2CO_2 + 3H_2O$ **(1)**
3. $Mg(s) + 2HNO_3(aq) \rightarrow Mg(NO_3)_2(aq) + H_2(g)$
   Formulae **(1)**, balancing **(1)**, state symbols **(1)**
4. (a) $Cl_2 + 2Br^- \rightarrow 2Cl^- + Br_2$ **(1)**
   (b) $Al^{3+} + 3OH^- \rightarrow Al(OH)_3$
   OH^- **(1)** 3 **(1)**
   (c) $Pb^{2+} + 2I^- \rightarrow PbI_2$
   I^- **(1)** 2 **(1)**

8–11. Atomic structure and the periodic table

1. $(11 \times 1.6726 \times 10^{-27}) + (12 \times 1.6750 \times 10^{-27}) +$
   $(11 \times 9.1094 \times 10^{-31})$ **(1)**
   $= 1.83986 \times 10^{-26} + 2.01 \times 10^{-26} + 1.002034 \times 10^{-29}$
   $= 8.50 \times 10^{-26}$ **(1)**
2. number of neutrons $= 8 + 0 = 8$ **(1)**
   number of electrons $= 9 + 1 = 10$ **(1)**
3. relative atomic mass
   $= \dfrac{(28 \times 92.17) + (29 \times 4.71) + (30 \times 3.12)}{100}$ **(1)**
   $= \dfrac{2580.76 + 136.59 + 93.6}{100}$
   $= 28.1$ **(1)**
4. Answers could include the following points **(6)**:
   - Elements are arranged in order of increasing number of protons / atomic number
   - A group is a vertical column of elements
   - All of the elements in the same group (from 1 to 7) have the same number of electrons in the outer shell of their elements
   - An example of a group and the number of electrons in the outer shell

- The atoms of the elements in group 0 have full outer shells of electrons
- A period is a horizontal row of elements
- All of the elements in the same period have the same number of occupied shells
- An example of a period and the number of occupied shells
- An example of a 'pair reversal', e.g. tellurium and iodine
- Explanation of the pair reversal in terms of relative atomic mass and atomic number

12–15. Bonding

1. Answers could include the following points (4):

Sodium 2.8.1

Sodium atoms lose 1 electron (per atom) / form Na^+

Oxygen 2.6

Oxygen atoms gain 2 electrons (per atom) / form O^{2-}

Sodium oxide contains two sodium ions for each oxide ion / is Na_2O

Marks can be awarded for labelled dot-and-cross diagrams

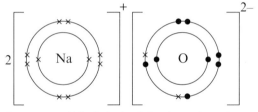

2. Answers could include the following points (6):

Similarities

- Both have strong electrostatic forces of attraction between oppositely charged particles / have strong bonding

Differences

- Magnesium has metallic bonding but chlorine has covalent bonding
- Magnesium is 2.8.2 but chlorine is 2.8.7
- Magnesium consists of positive ions in a sea of electrons but chlorine consists of molecules
- The electrons in the outer shell of magnesium are delocalised but the electrons in the outer shell of chlorine are shared
- Diagram or description of magnesium ions with positive charges in a sea of electrons
- The strong electrostatic forces are between positive ions and electrons in magnesium but between two nuclei and the shared pair of electrons in chlorine
- Diagram or description of a chlorine molecule with a shared pair of electrons

16–19. Structure, bonding and properties

1. Solid magnesium sulfate does not conduct electricity because the ions cannot move (1)

The ions can move when it is in an aqueous solution (1)

2. Both have high melting points because they are giant structures (1)

A lot of energy is needed to break the bonds and separate the particles (1)

Graphite has delocalised electrons but ceramics do not (1)

The delocalised electrons can move (through the layers) and carry the current (1)

3. Answers could include the following points (6):
- **A** is giant metallic
- **B** is giant ionic
- **C** is simple molecular covalent
- High melting point shows there is strong bonding and a giant structure in A
- Only metals (and graphite) conduct electricity when they are solids and graphite has an extremely high melting point so A has metallic bonding
- Ionic compounds conduct when they are molten but not when they are solid and they have high melting points
- Low melting point shows there are weak intermolecular forces, so there must be simple molecules in C
- Molecules are neutral so do not conduct electricity so C has covalent bonding

20–23. Acids, bases and salts

1. (a) Measure the volume of solution using a pipette instead of a measuring cylinder (1)

The hydrochloric acid should be in the burette and the sodium hydroxide solution in the conical flask (1)

Methyl orange is orange / peach at the end point, not green (1)

(b) Any two improvements explained from (2):
- Make sure there are no air bubbles in the burette / pipette (1) as this will affect the reading (1)
- Read the burette / pipette from the bottom of the meniscus (1) as this will give an accurate volume (1)
- Place the conical flask on a white tile (1) as this will make it easier to see the colour change (1)

- Add the hydrochloric acid dropwise near the end point **(1)** as this will make it easier to stop at exactly the right colour **(1)**
- Rinse the inside of the flask with distilled or deionised water before the end point **(1)** to make sure all the reactants are mixed together **(1)**

2. (a) Barium nitrate or barium chloride solution **(1)**

   Any soluble sulfate, e.g. sodium sulfate or potassium sulfate **(1)**

   (b) (i) Lead chloride **(1)**

   (ii) $Pb^{2+}(aq) + 2Cl^-(aq) \rightarrow PbCl_2(s)$

   formulae **(1)** balancing **(1)** state symbols **(1)**

   (iii) Filter **(1)**

   Wash the precipitate with water **(1)**

   Dry the precipitate by placing in a warm oven / on a radiator / on a sunny windowsill / other suitable method of drying **(1)**

24–25. Calculations with masses

1. $M_r = 56 + 2(16 + 1) = 90$ **(1)**

   $180\,kg = 180\,000\,g / 1.8 \times 10^5\,g$

   amount $= \dfrac{1.8 \times 10^5}{90} = 2000\,mol / 2 \times 10^3\,mol$ **(1)**

2. (a) amount Mg $= \dfrac{1.2}{24} = 0.05\,mol$ **(1)**

   $M_r\ H_2SO_4 = (2 \times 1) + 32 + (4 \times 16) = 98$ **(1)**

   amount $H_2SO_4 = \dfrac{6.0}{98} = 0.0612\,mol$ **(1)**

   mol ratio Mg : H_2SO_4 = 1:1
   0.05 mol Mg reacts with 0.05 mol H_2SO_4 so the sulfuric acid is in excess **(1)**

   (b) theoretical amount of $MgSO_4$ = amount Mg used = 0.05 mol

   $M_r\ MgSO_4 = 24 + 32 + (4 \times 16) = 120$ **(1)**

   theoretical mass of $MgSO_4 = 0.05 \times 120$
   $= 6.0\,g$ **(1)**

   percentage yield $= \dfrac{actual\ mass}{theoretical\ mass} \times 100$

   $= \dfrac{5.2}{6.0} \times 100 = 86.7\%$ **(1)**

   TE on amount of Mg calculated in (a)

26–27. Calculations with gas volumes

1. 1 mol of ethane reacts with $3\frac{1}{2}$ mol of oxygen to produce 2 mol of carbon dioxide

   so 100 cm³ of ethane reacts with /
   $100 \times 3\frac{1}{2} = 350\,cm^3$ of oxygen to produce
   $100 \times 2 = 200\,cm^3$ of carbon dioxide **(1)**

there will be $500 - 350 = 150\,cm^3$ oxygen left **(1)**
final gas volume = volume of oxygen left + volume of carbon dioxide produced = 150 + 200
$= 350\,cm^3$ **(1)**

2. amount of gas $= \dfrac{12}{24} = 0.5\,mol$

   0.5 mol of gas has a mass of 22 g

   so relative formula mass $= \dfrac{mass}{mol}$

   $= \dfrac{22}{0.5} = 44$ **(1)**

3. amount of sulfur dioxide $= \dfrac{120}{24\,000}$

   $= \dfrac{0.005}{5 \times 10^{-3}\,mol}$ **(1)**

   number of sulfur dioxide molecules =
   $0.005 \times 6.02 \times 10^{23} = 3.01 \times 10^{21}$ **(1)**

   each molecule contains 3 atoms so number of atoms $= 3 \times 3.01 \times 10^{21} = 9.03 \times 10^{21}$ **(1)**

28–29. Calculations with concentrations of solutions

1. amount of HCl $= \dfrac{0.150 \times 35.0}{1000} = 5.25 \times 10^{-3}\,mol$ **(1)**

   1 mol KOH reacts with 1 mol HCl so amount KOH $= 5.25 \times 10^{-3}\,mol$

   concentration KOH $= \dfrac{5.25 \times 10^{-3} \times 1000}{25.0}$
   $= 0.210\,mol\,dm^{-3}$ **(1)**

2. amount of $H_2SO_4 = \dfrac{0.050 \times 27.5}{1000}$
   $= 1.375 \times 10^{-3}\,mol$ **(1)**

   2 mol NaOH reacts with 1 mol H_2SO_4 so amount NaOH $= 2 \times 1.375 \times 10^{-3} = 2.75 \times 10^{-3}\,mol$ **(1)**

   concentration NaOH $= \dfrac{2.75 \times 10^{-3} \times 1000}{25.0}$
   $= 0.110\,mol\,dm^{-3}$ **(1)**

   $M_r\ NaOH = 23 + 16 + 1 = 40$ **(1)**

   concentration NaOH $= 0.110 \times 40$
   $= 4.40\,g\,dm^{-3}$ **(1)**

30–33. All mole calculations

1. (a) amount of $Ca(NO_3)_2$

   $= \dfrac{2.05}{(40 + (2 \times 14) + (6 \times 16))} = 0.0125\,mol$ **(1)**

   from the balanced equation, 2 mol $Ca(NO_3)_2$ produces 5 mol of gas (4 mol NO_2 + 1 mol O_2) so 0.0125 mol $Ca(NO_3)_2$ will produce
   $0.0125 \times \dfrac{5}{2} = 0.0125\,mol\ gas$ **(1)**

   volume of gas produced $= 0.03125 \times 24\,000$
   $= 750\,cm^3$ **(1)**

   (b) percentage yield $= \dfrac{actual\ yield}{theoretical\ yield} \times 100$

   $= \dfrac{675}{750} \times 100 = 90\%$ **(1)**

(c) M_r of $CaO = 40 + 16 = 56$ and
M_r of $NO_2 = 14 + (2 \times 16) = 46$ and
M_r of $O_2 = 2 \times 16 = 32$ **(1)**
total M_r of all products =
$(2 \times 56) + (4 \times 46) + 32 = 328$ **(1)**

atom economy

$$= \frac{2 \times M_r \text{ of } CaO}{\text{total } M_r \text{ of all products}} \times 100$$

$$= \frac{2 \times 56}{328} \times 100 = 34.1\% \text{ (1)}$$

2. (a) M_r of $MgCO_3 = 24 + 12 + (3 \times 16) = 84$ **(1)**
amount of $MgCO_3 = \frac{2.25}{84} = 0.0268$ mol **(1)**
from the balanced equation, 1 mol $MgCO_3$
reacts with 2 mol of HCl, so 0.0268 mol
$MgCO_3$ reacts with $2 \times 0.0268 = 0.0536$ mol
HCl **(1)**

volume of HCl

$$= \frac{\text{amount in mol}}{\text{concentration in mol dm}^{-3}} = \frac{0.0536}{2.50}$$

$= 0.02144$ dm^3
volume of HCl $= 1000 \times 0.02144$
$= 21.4$ cm^3 **(1)**

(b) From the balanced equation, 1 mol of
$MgCO_3$ produces 1 mol of CO_2, so 0.0268
mol $MgCO_3$ produces 0.0268 mol CO_2

volume of $CO_2 = 0.0268 \times 24\,000$

$= 643.2 / 643$ cm^3 **(1)**

34–37. Electrochemistry

1. $2H_2(g) \rightarrow 2H^+(aq) + 4e^-$ **(1)** oxidation because the
hydrogen atoms lose electrons **(1)**

2. Comparison: both experiments produce copper at
the cathode **(1)**
$Cu^{2+}(aq) + 2e^- \rightarrow Cu(s)$ **(1)**
Difference: when copper sulfate solution is
electrolysed using graphite electrodes, oxygen is
produced at the anode **(1)**
$4OH^-(aq) \rightarrow O_2(g) + 2H_2O(l) + 4e^-$ **(1)**
When copper sulfate solution is electrolysed using
copper electrodes, copper atoms form copper ions
that dissolve in the solution **(1)**
$Cu(s) \rightarrow Cu^{2+}(aq) + 2e^-$ **(1)**

3. Answers could include the following points **(6)**:
- chloride ions are attracted to the anode
- hydroxide ions are attracted to the anode
- chloride ions lose two electrons to form
chlorine gas
- $2Cl^-(aq) \rightarrow Cl_2(g) + 2e^-$
- this is an oxidation reaction
- hydrogen ions are attracted to the cathode

- sodium ions are attracted to the cathode
- hydrogen ions gain electrons to form
hydrogen gas
- $2H^+(aq) + 2e^- \rightarrow H_2(g)$
- this is a reduction reaction
- overall equation: $2NaCl(aq) + 2H_2O(l) \rightarrow$
$Cl_2(g) + H_2(g) + 2NaOH(aq)$

38–41. Metals

1. Physical property: iron has a higher melting
point / boiling point / density than sodium **(1)**
Chemical property: iron forms coloured
compounds but sodium forms colourless / white
compounds or iron can be used as a catalyst and
sodium is not a catalyst **(1)**

2. Magnesium oxidises / forms positive ions **(1)** more
easily than iron so oxygen reacts with magnesium
instead of iron **(1)**
$Mg \rightarrow Mg^{2+} + 2e^-$ **(1)**

3. Gold atoms / ions are all the same size and
arranged in layers. **(1)** They can slide over each
other easily. **(1)** Alloy contains other metals with
atoms of different sizes to gold atoms. **(1)** This
disrupts the layers in gold and prevents them
from sliding over each other. **(1)**

4. Answers could include the following points **(6)**:
- Magnesium is higher in the reactivity series
than iron
- Magnesium is more reactive than carbon
- Carbon is more reactive than iron
- Iron oxide is reduced by heating with carbon
but magnesium chloride cannot be reduced by
heating with carbon
- Magnesium can be extracted by the electrolysis
of molten magnesium chloride
- Electrolysis is a more powerful method
of reduction
- Energy has to be supplied to provide the heat
needed for the reaction between iron oxide
and carbon
- Energy has to be supplied to keep the
magnesium chloride molten and for the
electrolysis process

42–45. Reversible reactions and equilibria

1. An increase in temperature favours the
endothermic reaction **(1)**
The forwards reaction is endothermic **(1)**
So the equilibrium mixture turns darker brown
as the concentration of nitrogen dioxide
increases **(1)**

2. Dilute sulfuric acid contains H^+ ions **(1)**

When H^+ ions are added, the equilibrium position moves in the direction away from the added ions, i.e. in the forward direction **(1)**

So the mixture turns orange **(1)**

3. Answers could include the following points **(6)**:

- Increasing the temperature favours the endothermic reaction
- The backwards reaction is endothermic
- The equilibrium position will move to the left and the equilibrium yield of sulfur trioxide will decrease
- However, increasing the temperature increases the rate of reaction
- Because the energy of the particles increases
- And there will be more frequent successful collisions
- Increasing the pressure favours the reaction producing the fewer number of moles of gas molecules
- There are 3 moles of gas molecules on the left of the equation and 2 moles on the right / there is a decrease in the number of moles of gas molecules in the forward reaction
- So the equilibrium position will move to the right and the equilibrium yield of sulfur trioxide will increase
- Increasing the pressure also increases the rate of reaction
- Because the molecules will be closer together and collide more frequently

46–49. Groups in the periodic table

1. When potassium chloride solution is added to bromine water:

- the mixture stays orange / yellow or there is no (colour) change **(1)**
- showing that no reaction has taken place **(1)**
- so chlorine is more reactive than bromine **(1)**

When potassium iodide solution is added to bromine water:

- the mixture turns brown **(1)**
- showing that iodine has been formed **(1)**
- so bromine is more reactive than iodine **(1)**

2. Answers could include the following points **(6)**:

- The reactivity of both groups depends on the number of electrons in the outer shell of the elements
- The size of the atoms increases on going down both groups

- All elements in group 1 have 1 electron in the outer shell of their atoms but all elements in group 7 have 7 electrons in the outer shell of their atoms
- During a reaction group 1 atoms lose the outer electron but group 7 atoms gain an electron (into the outer shell)
- Group 1 atoms form positive ions but group 7 atoms form negative ions
- Descending group 1, the force of attraction between the nucleus and the outer electron decreases so it is easier to lose the electron but in group 7, the force of attraction between the nucleus and the incoming electron decreases so it is harder to gain an electron
- So reactivity increases down group 1 but decreases down group 7

50–53. Rates of reaction

1. (a) Suitable scale so that the plotted points occupy at least half the paper in both directions **(1)**

Points plotted accurately ± half a small square and joined by a smooth curve **(1)**

Axes labelled with measurements and units **(1)**

(b) (i) Tangent drawn at time = 0 **(1)**

(ii) Values of y and x from graph and tangent, e.g. $78\,cm^3$ and $60\,s$ **(1)**

Rate calculated, e.g. $\frac{78}{60} = 1.3$ **(1)**

Units $cm^3\,s^{-1}$ or cm^3/s **(1)**

(c) Line drawn steeper than original line **(1)** and levelling off at the same volume **(1)**

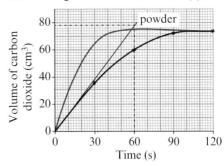

(d) $M_r\,CaCO_3 = 40 + 12 + (3 \times 16) = 100$

Amount $CaCO_3 = \frac{6.0}{100} = 0.06\,mol$ **(1)**

Amount $HCl = 50 \times \frac{0.2}{1000} = 0.01\,mol$ **(1)**

$0.06\,mol\ CaCO_3$ needs $2 \times 0.06 = 0.12\,mol$ HCl for reaction

There is only $0.01\,mol$ HCl present so $CaCO_3$ is in excess **(1)**

2. Answers could include the following points **(6)**:
- A reaction occurs when particle collisions have (at least) the activation energy
- The rate of reaction increases when the energy of collisions increases and/or the frequency of collisions
- The rate of reaction is inversely proportional to the time taken (for the magnesium ribbon to react)
- Experiment 2 was carried out at the same temperature as experiment 1 but the concentration of sulfuric acid was halved
- There are fewer particles in the same volume
- So the frequency of collisions between the acid particles and the magnesium decreases
- And the time taken for the magnesium to react increases / doubles
- Experiment 3 had the same concentration of sulfuric acid as experiment 2 but the temperature was higher
- The particles have more (kinetic) energy so move faster
- So the frequency of collisions between the acid particles and magnesium increases
- And the energy of the collisions increases
- So the time taken for the magnesium to react decreases
- Changing the temperature has a bigger effect than changing the concentration

54–57. Heat energy changes

1. (a) Bonds broken: Bonds made:

$$C-C = \quad 347 \quad 4 \times C=O = 4 \times 805$$
$$5 \times C-H = 5 \times 413 \quad 6 \times O-H = \underline{6 \times 464}$$
$$C-O = \quad 358 \quad \text{Total} \quad\quad 6004 \text{ (1)}$$
$$O-H = \quad 464$$
$$3 \times O=O = \underline{3 \times 498}$$
$$\text{Total} \quad\quad 4728 \text{ (1)}$$

Energy change = 4728 – 6004 **(1)**
          = $-1276\,kJ\,mol^{-1}$ **(1)**

It would be acceptable to leave out the O–H bond on the left and have 5 × O–H bonds on the right.

(b)

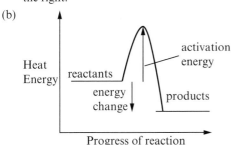

Diagram showing 'hump' and products at lower level than reactants **(1)**
Activation energy labelled **(1)**
Energy change labelled **(1)**

2. (a) Any 3 from: measure the temperature of the water before and after heating, stir the water, use draft shields around the alcohol burner, put the cap back on the burner before reweighing it, use a copper can / calorimeter

(b) Volume of water **(1)**, size of the flame **(1)** and height of beaker above the wick **(1)**

(c) ethanol:
mass burned = 156.64 − 155.82 = 0.82 g
temperature rise = 41 – 20 = 21 °C
temperature rise/g = $\frac{21}{0.82}$ = 26 °C/g **(1)**
propanol:
mass burned = 163.20 – 162.81 = 0.39 g
temperature rise = 39 – 20 = 19 °C
temperature rise/g = $\frac{19}{0.39}$ = 49 °C/g **(1)**
It is better to give the answers to 2 SF as the temperatures are only given to 2 SF
ethanol:
M_r = (2 × 12) + (5 × 1) + 16 + 1 = 46
temperature rise/mol = $\frac{25.61}{46}$ = 0.56 °C/mol **(1)**
propanol:
M_r = (3 × 12) + (7 × 1) + 16 + 1 = 60
temperature rise/mol = $\frac{48.72}{60}$ = 0.82 °C/mol **(1)**

58–61. Hydrocarbons

1. (a)

Name	Formula	Structure
cyclopropane	C_3H_6 **(1)**	
cyclobutane	C_4H_8	
cyclopentane	C_5H_{10} **(1)**	

75

(b) C_7H_{14} **(1)** because the general formula is C_nH_{2n} or the number of hydrogen atoms is double the number of carbon atoms **(1)**

(c) $C_4H_8 + 6O_2 \rightarrow 4CO_2 + 4H_2O$
formulae **(1)** balancing **(1)**

2. (a) (i) mass of hydrogen $= 100 - 82.8 = 17.2\,g$ **(1)**

	C	H
mass (g)	82.8	17.2
A_r	12	1
amount (mol)	$\frac{82.8}{12} = 6.9$	$\frac{17.2}{1} = 17.2$
divide by smaller	$\frac{6.9}{6.9} = 1$	$\frac{17.2}{6.9} = 2.5$
simplest whole number ratio	2	5 **(1)**

empirical formula is C_2H_5 **(1)**

(ii) empirical formula mass
$= (2 \times 12) + (5 \times 1) = 29$ **(1)**

divide M_r by empirical formula mass $\frac{58}{29} = 2$
molecular formula is C_4H_{10} **(1)**

(b) 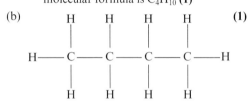 **(1)**

3. The hydrocarbon must be an alkene / contain C=C as it decolourises bromine **(1)**

General formula of an alkene is C_nH_{2n} and the M_r of CH_2 is $12 + (2 \times 1) = 14$ **(1)**
$\frac{84}{14} = 6$
So the alkene is C_6H_{12} **(1)**
$C_6H_{12} + Br_2 \rightarrow C_6H_{12}Br_2$ **(1)**

62–65. Alcohols and carboxylic acids

1.

Name	Formula	Structure	
ethanol	C_2H_5OH	H H | | H—C—C—O—H | | H H	**(1)**
propanol	C_3H_7OH	H H H | | | H—C—C—C—O—H | | | H H H	**(1)**

methanoic acid	HCOOH	$H-C{\Large{<}}{}^{O}_{O-H}$	**(1)**
butanoic acid	C_3H_7COOH	H H H | | | H—C—C—C—C${\large<}{}^{O}_{O-H}$ | | | H H H	**(1)**

2. (a) effervescence or fizzing or bubbles (because carbon dioxide gas is produced) or calcium carbonate disappears / gets smaller **(1)**

(b) $2CH_3COOH(aq) + CaCO_3(s) \rightarrow$
$Ca(CH_3COO)_2(aq) + H_2O(l) + CO_2(g)$
formulae **(1)**, balancing **(1)**, state symbols **(1)**

3. (a)

	C	H	O
mass (g)	1.44	0.32	0.64
A_r	12	1	16
amount (mol)	$\frac{1.44}{12} = 0.12$	$\frac{0.32}{1} = 0.32$	$\frac{0.64}{16} = 0.04$ **(1)**
divide by smaller	$\frac{0.12}{0.04} = 3$	$\frac{0.32}{0.04} = 8$	$\frac{0.04}{0.04} = 1$ **(1)**

empirical formula is C_3H_8O **(1)**
empirical formula mass $= (3 \times 12) + (8 \times 1) + (1 \times 16) = 60$

this is the same as the M_r so the molecular formula is C_3H_8O **(1)**

(b) **A** only has one oxygen atom and can be oxidised so it must be an alcohol **(1)**
A is propanol **(1)**
Propanol can be oxidised to propanoic acid **(1)** so **B** is propanoic acid **(1)**

(c) $2C_2H_5COOH(aq) + Mg(s) \rightarrow$
$Mg(C_2H_5COO)_2(aq) + H_2(g)$
formulae **(1)**, balancing **(1)**, state symbols **(1)**

66–67. Polymerisation

1.

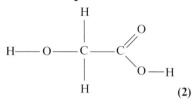 **(2)**

OH group **(1)**, COOH group and rest of structure **(1)**

2.

H	CH₃	H	CH₃

$$-C-C-C-C-$$

H	CH₃	H	CH₃

(2)

4 carbon atoms with extension bonds (1),
rest of structure correct (1)

68–69. Qualitative analysis

(a)

Test	Observation	Conclusion
Test 1 Carry out a flame test on **A**	A lilac flame is seen	The formula of the cation identified by this test is K^+ (1)
Test 2 Add aqueous sodium hydroxide to **A** and warm the mixture	A gas was given off which turned damp red litmus blue	The name of the gas is Ammonia (1) The formula of the cation identified by this test is NH_4^+ (1)
Test 3 Add a few drops of dilute hydrochloric acid to an aqueous solution of **A**, then add a few drops of aqueous barium chloride	A white precipitate forms	The name of the white precipitate is barium sulfate (1) The formula of the anion is SO_4^{2-} (1)

(b) KNH_4SO_4 or NH_4KSO_4 (1)

(c) (i) Hydrochloric acid reacts with carbonates (1) and prevents them from forming a precipitate with aqueous barium chloride (1)

(ii) Sulfate ions (from sulfuric acid) react with barium ions (1) to form a precipitate of barium sulfate (1)

Match to the Revise Pearson Edexcel GCSE (9–1) Combined Science Higher Revision Guide

If you are doing Pearson Edexcel GCSE (9–1) Combined Science Higher exam, use the table below to match the pages and knowledge check questions to the Revise Pearson Edexcel GCSE (9–1) Combined Science Higher Revision Guide. The circled knowledge check questions are Pearson Edexcel GCSE (9–1) Chemistry Higher only questions.

Chemistry Nail it! pages	Knowledge check question	Combined Science RG pages
6–7	1, 2, 5	87–89, 97
8–11	3	91–95
12–15	4, 7	96, 97, 99, 103
16–19	6, 8, 9	98, 100–104, 111
20–23	15, 16, 17, 18	120–127
24–25	10, 11, 13, 14, (28)	105–108, 110
26–27	24, 25	
28–29	12, (24), (25), (26), (27)	109
30–33		110
34–37	19, 20	128–131
38–41	21, 22	132–135
42–45	29	141–142
46–49	30	143–148
50–53	31	149–151
54–57	32	152–154
58–61	(33)	155–162
62–65	(35)	
66–67	(34)	
68–69	(36)	

Published by Pearson Education Limited, 80 Strand, London, WC2R 0RL.

www.pearsonschoolsandfecolleges.co.uk

Copies of official specifications for all Pearson qualifications may be found on the website: qualifications.pearson.com

Text and illustrations © Pearson Education Ltd 2019
Typeset by Newgen KnowledgeWorks Pvt. Ltd., Chennai, India
Produced and illustrated by Newgen
Cover illustration by Miriam Sturdee

The right of Sue Robilliard to be identified as author of this work has been asserted by her in accordance with the Copyright, Designs and Patents Act 1988.

First published 2019

22 21 20 19
10 9 8 7 6 5 4 3 2 1

British Library Cataloguing in Publication Data
A catalogue record for this book is available from the British Library

ISBN 978 1 292 29427 8

Printed in Slovakia by Neografia

Notes from the publisher

1. While the publishers have made every attempt to ensure that advice on the qualification and its assessment is accurate, the official specification and associated assessment guidance materials are the only authoritative source of information and should always be referred to for definitive guidance.

Pearson examiners have not contributed to any sections in this resource relevant to examination papers for which they have responsibility.

2. Pearson has robust editorial processes, including answer and fact checks, to ensure the accuracy of the content in this publication, and every effort is made to ensure this publication is free of errors. We are, however, only human, and occasionally errors do occur. Pearson is not liable for any misunderstandings that arise as a result of errors in this publication, but it is our priority to ensure that the content is accurate. If you spot an error, please do contact us at resourcescorrections@pearson.com so we can make sure it is corrected.